Vocabulary Workshop
New Edition

Level H

Jerome Shostak

Series Consultants

Sylvia A. Rendón, Ph.D.
Coord., Secondary Reading
Cypress-Fairbanks I.S.D.
Houston, Texas

Mel H. Farberman
Director of English
Language Arts, K–12
Bay Shore U.F.S.D.
Bay Shore, New York

John Heath, Ph.D.
Department of Classics
Santa Clara University
Santa Clara, California

Sadlier-Oxford
A Division of William H. Sadlier, Inc.

Reviewers

The publisher wishes to thank for their comments and suggestions the following teachers and administrators, who read portions of the series prior to publication.

Photo Credits

Corbis/Bettmann: 27, 41, 71, 104; W. Perry Conway: 34; Mark E. Gibson: 57; Paul Almasy: 149; Gordon Whitten: 156; Used with permission of the Estate of Zora Neale Hurston: 170; Roger Antrobus: 182. *Getty Images*/The Image Bank/Terje Rakke: 83; The Image Bank/J H Pete Carmichael: 116. *The Granger Collection*: 64. *The Library of Congress, Prints & Photographs Division*/Dorothea Lange, Reproduction No. LC-USF34-9095: 163. Jacob Lawrence, *The Migration of the Negro, No. 18: The migration gained in momentum.* Casein tempera on hardboard, 18 x 12 in. Museum of Modern Art, New York. Artwork © 2005 Gwendolyn Knight Lawrence, courtesy of The Jacob and Gwendolyn Lawrence Foundation: 97. *National Geographic Society*/Kenneth Garrett: 123. *PhotoEdit*/Richard Hutchings: 90; Dennis MacDonald: 137. *The Viesti Collection*/Joe Viesti: 130.

Printed in the United States of America.
ISBN: 0-8215-7113-3
123456789/09 08 07 06 05

PREFACE

For over five decades, VOCABULARY WORKSHOP has proven a highly successful tool for guiding systematic vocabulary growth and developing vocabulary skills. It has also been shown to be a valuable help to students preparing for standardized tests. This New Edition of VOCABULARY WORKSHOP has been prepared in recognition of important changes to these tests, with the introduction of two features designed to address the new emphasis on writing skills, including grammar, and reading skills on those tests.

A new **Vocabulary for Comprehension** section appears in each of the five Reviews. This two-page feature is modeled on the reading sections of standardized tests, and as in those tests, presents reading comprehension questions, including specific vocabulary-related ones, based on a reading passage. (For more on Vocabulary for Comprehension, see page 13.)

Following Vocabulary for Comprehension in each of the Reviews is another new feature called **Grammar in Context**. This one-page exercise is linked to the reading passage that precedes it, referring to a grammar or usage topic illustrated in the passage and then reviewing that topic with a brief explanation and practice questions. (For more on Grammar in Context, see page 16.)

The 15 Units that form the core of VOCABULARY WORKSHOP remain unchanged. Each of the Units comprises a five-part lesson consisting of **Definitions, Completing the Sentence, Synonyms and Antonyms, Choosing the Right Word**, and **Vocabulary in Context**. Together, these exercises provide multiple and varied exposures to the taught words, an approach that has been shown to be consistent with and supportive of research-based findings in vocabulary instruction.

Enrichment and vocabulary-building exercises also remain in the form of **Building with Classical Roots, Word Associations**, and **Word Families** in the Reviews, and **Analogies** and **Enriching Your Vocabulary** in the Cumulative Reviews.

In this Level of Vocabulary Workshop you will study 300 key words. The words in this Level, as well as all of the other Levels of this series, have been selected on the following bases: currency and general usefulness; frequency of appearance on recognized vocabulary lists; applicability to, and appearance on, standardized tests; and current grade-level research. In addition to the 300 key words, you will be introduced to hundreds of other words in the form of synonyms, antonyms, and other relatives. Mastery of these words will make you a better reader, a better writer and speaker, and better prepared for the challenges of standardized tests.

CONTENTS

PRONUNCIATION KEY

The pronunciation is indicated for every basic word introduced in this book. The symbols used for this purpose, as listed below, are similar to those appearing in most standard dictionaries of recent vintage. (Pronunciation keys and given pronunciations sometimes differ from dictionary to dictionary.) The author has consulted a large number of dictionaries for this purpose but has relied primarily on *Webster's Third New International Dictionary* and *The Random House Dictionary of the English Language (Unabridged).*

There are, of course, many English words for which two (or more) pronunciations are commonly accepted. In virtually all cases where such words occur in this book, the author has sought to make things easier for the student by giving just one pronunciation. The only significant exception occurs when the pronunciation changes in accordance with a shift in the part of speech. Thus we would indicate that *project* in the verb form is pronounced prə jekt', and in the noun form, präj' ekt.

It is believed that these relatively simple pronunciation guides will be readily usable by the student. It should be emphasized, however, that the *best* way to learn the pronunciation of a word is to listen to and imitate an educated speaker.

Vowels						
	ā	lake	e	stress	ü	loot, new
	a	mat	ī	knife	ù	foot, pull
	â	care	i	sit	ə	jumping, broken
	ä	bark, bottle	ō	flow	ər	bird, better
	aù	doubt	ô	all, cord		
	ē	beat, wordy	oi	oil		

Consonants						
	ch	child, lecture	s	cellar	wh	what
	g	give	sh	shun	y	yearn
	j	gentle, bridge	th	thank	z	is
	ŋ	sing	th	those	zh	measure

All other consonants are sounded as in the alphabet.

Stress The accent mark *follows* the syllable receiving the major stress: en rich'

Abbreviations					
	adj.	adjective	n.	noun	prep.	preposition
	adv.	adverb	part.	participle	v.	verb
	int.	interjection	pl.	plural		

THE VOCABULARY OF VOCABULARY

There are some interesting and useful words that are employed to describe and identify words. The exercises that follow will help you to check and strengthen your knowledge of this "vocabulary of vocabulary."

Denotation and Connotation

The **denotation** of a word is its specific dictionary meaning. Here are a few examples:

Word	Denotation
benevolent	kind or charitable
callous	emotionally hardened or unfeeling
reiterate	repeat

The **connotation** of a word is its **tone**—that is, the emotions or associations it normally arouses in people using, hearing, or reading it. Depending on what these feelings are, the connotation of a word may be *favorable* (*positive*) or *unfavorable* (*negative, pejorative*). A word that does not normally arouse strong feelings of any kind has a *neutral* connotation. Here are some examples of words with different connotations:

Word	Connotation
benevolent	favorable
callous	unfavorable
reiterate	neutral

Exercises   *In the space provided, label the connotation of each of the following words* **F** *for "favorable,"* **U** *for "unfavorable," or* **N** *for "neutral."*

_____ **1.** precedent   _____ **3.** contentious   _____ **5.** deride

_____ **2.** deft   _____ **4.** alacrity   _____ **6.** allocate

Literal and Figurative Usage

When a word is used in a **literal** sense, it is being employed in its strict (or primary) dictionary meaning in a situation (or context) that "makes sense" from a purely logical or realistic point of view. For example:

The corn was not harvested while it was still *green*.

In this sentence, *green* is employed literally. Corn that is not yet ripe is green.

Sometimes words are used in a symbolic or nonliteral way in situations that do not "make sense" from a purely logical or realistic point of view. We call this nonliteral application of a word a **figurative** or **metaphorical** usage. For example:

It takes a *green* young rookie years to become a seasoned, streetwise veteran.

In this sentence, *green* is not being used in a literal sense. That is, *green* is being used figuratively to indicate that the young rookie has not yet gained maturity and experience.

Exercises *In the space provided, write **L** for "literal" or **F** for "figurative" next to each of the following sentences to show how the italicized expression is being used.*

_____ **1.** The *musty* odor in the dark, damp cellar was most unpleasant.

_____ **2.** Teenagers sometimes dismiss their parents' ideas as *musty* and antiquated.

_____ **3.** Only a singer with a *supple* voice can do full justice to the elaborate music of the baroque era.

Synonyms

A **synonym** is a word that has *the same* or *almost the same* meaning as another word. Here are some examples:

guile—trickery   delete—remove
brash—brazen   somber—gloomy
skulk—lurk   askew—lopsided

Exercises   *In each of the following groups, circle the word that is most nearly the **synonym** of the word in **boldface** type.*

1. pinnacle	**2. placate**	**3. dearth**	**4. tentative**
a. article	a. mollify	a. surplus	a. uncertain
b. viewpoint	b. cure	b. failure	b. thoughtful
c. summit	c. ridicule	c. supply	c. conclusive
d. pause	d. provoke	d. scarcity	d. interested

Antonyms

An **antonym** is a word that means *the opposite* of or *almost the opposite* of another word. Here are some examples:

elated—depressed   dour—cheery
chastise—commend   repose—exertion
disperse—collect   harmony—rancor

Exercises   *In each of the following groups, circle the word that is most nearly the **antonym** of the word in **boldface** type.*

1. stolid	**2. deride**	**3. limpid**	**4. urbane**
a. emotional	a. forestall	a. blatant	a. naive
b. relaxed	b. extol	b. colorful	b. suave
c. impassive	c. amuse	c. murky	c. crude
d. flighty	d. decide	d. subtle	d. diffident

VOCABULARY STRATEGY: USING CONTEXT

How do you go about finding the meaning of an unknown or unfamiliar word that you come across in your reading? You might look the word up in a dictionary, of course, provided one is at hand. But there are two other useful strategies that you might employ to find the meaning of a word that you do not know at all or that is used in a way that you do not recognize. One strategy is to analyze the **structure** or parts of the word. (See pages 11 and 12 for more on this strategy.) The other strategy is to try to figure out the meaning of the word by reference to context.

When we speak of the **context** of a word, we mean the printed text of which that word is part. By studying the context, we may find **clues** that lead us to its meaning. We might find a clue in the immediate sentence or phrase in which the word appears (and sometimes in adjoining sentences or phrases, too); or we might find a clue in the topic or subject matter of the passage in which the word appears; or we might even find a clue in the physical features of a page itself. (Photographs, illustrations, charts, graphs, captions, and headings are some examples of such features.)

One way to use context as a strategy is to ask yourself what you know already about the topic or subject matter in question. By applying what you have learned before about deserts, for example, you would probably be able to figure out that the word *arid* in the phrase "the arid climate of the desert" means "dry."

The **Vocabulary in Context** exercises that appear in the Units and the **Vocabulary for Comprehension** and the **Choosing the Right Meaning** exercises that appear in the Reviews and Cumulative Reviews provide practice in using context to determine the meaning of given words.

When you do the various word-omission exercises in this book, look for **context clues** built into the sentence or passage to guide you to the correct answer. Three types of context clues appear in the exercises in this book.

A **restatement clue** consists of a *synonym* for, or a *definition* of, the missing word. For example:

A _____ person may be too timid to speak to strangers at a party.

a. disheveled   (b. diffident)   c. brash   d. droll

In this sentence, *timid* is a synonym of the missing word, *diffident*, and acts as a restatement clue for it.

A **contrast clue** consists of an *antonym* for, or a phrase that means the *opposite* of, the missing word. For example:

Although the actor's laughter seemed (**spontaneous,** raucous), I knew that it had been carefully rehearsed.

In this sentence, *rehearsed* is an antonym of the missing word, *spontaneous*. This is confirmed by the presence of the words *although* and *seemed*, which indicate that the answer must be the opposite of *rehearsed*.

An **inference clue** implies but does not directly state the meaning of the missing word or words. For example:

Only _____ amounts of rain this spring will _____ the severe drought in the northeastern states.

a. mandatory . . . fathom
b. palatable . . . waive

c. copious . . . alleviate
d. opulent . . . stipulate

This sentence contains inference clues: (a) the words *severe drought* suggest that the amount of rain needed must be *copious*; (b) the phrase *only copious amounts of rain* suggests the word *alleviate* because that is what so much rain will do to a drought.

Exercises   *Use context clues to choose the word or words that complete each of the following sentences or sets of sentences.*

1. Some people are so _____ that they are always ready to argue about anything whatsoever.

a. secretive
b. predictable

c. contentious
d. sneaky

2. I don't understand how someone who is normally so (**meticulous, tepid**) could do such a careless job.

3. Utter _____ erupted when the noisy, _____ crowd saw their adored rock star alight from the limousine.

a. compassion . . . grotesque
b. conflagration . . . obnoxious

c. pandemonium . . . raucous
d. animosity . . . belligerent

VOCABULARY STRATEGY: WORD STRUCTURE

One important way to build your vocabulary is to learn the meaning of word parts that make up many English words. These word parts consist of **prefixes**, **suffixes**, and **roots**, or **bases**. A useful strategy for determining the meaning of an unknown word is to "take apart" the word and think about the parts. For example, when you look at the word parts in the word *invisible,* you find the prefix *in-* ("not") + the root *-vis-* ("see") + the suffix *-ible* ("capable of"). From knowing the meanings of the parts of this word, you can figure out that *invisible* means "not capable of being seen."

Following is a list of common prefixes. Knowing the meaning of a prefix can help you determine the meaning of a word in which the prefix appears.

Prefix	Meaning	Sample Words
bi-	two	bicycle
com-, con-	together, with	compatriot, contact
de-, dis-	lower, opposite	devalue, disloyal
fore-, pre-	before, ahead of time	forewarn, preplan
il-, im-, in-, ir, non-, un-	not	illegal, impossible, inactive, irregular, nonsense, unable
in-, im-	in, into	inhale, import
mid-	middle	midway
mis-	wrongly, badly	mistake, misbehave
re-	again, back	redo, repay
sub-	under, less than	submarine, subzero
super-	above, greater than	superimpose, superstar
tri-	three	triangle

Following is a list of common suffixes. Knowing the meaning and grammatical function of a suffix can help you determine the meaning of a word.

Noun Suffix	Meaning	Sample Nouns
-acy, -ance, -ence, -hood, -ity, -ment, -ness, -ship	state, quality, or condition of, act or process of	adequacy, attendance, persistence, neighborhood, activity, judgment, brightness, friendship
-ant, -eer, -ent, -er, -ian, -ier, -ist, -or	one who does or makes something	contestant, auctioneer, resident, banker, comedian, financier, dentist, doctor
-ation, -ition, -ion	act or result of	organization, imposition, election

Verb Suffix	Meaning	Sample Verbs
-ate	to become, produce, or treat	validate, salivate, chlorinate
-en	to make, cause to be	weaken
-fy, -ify, -ize	to cause, make	liquefy, glorify, legalize

Adjective Suffix	Meaning	Sample Adjectives
-able, -ible	able, capable of	believable, incredible
-al, -ic,	relating to, characteristic of	natural, romantic
-ful, -ive, -ous	full of, given to, marked by	beautiful, protective, poisonous
-ish, -like	like, resembling	foolish, childlike
-less	lacking, without	careless

A **base** or **root** is the main part of a word to which prefixes and suffixes may be added. Many roots come to English from Latin, such as *-socio-,* meaning "society," or from Greek, such as *-logy-,* meaning "the study of." Knowing Greek and Latin roots can help you determine the meaning of a word such as *sociology,* which means "the study of society."

In the **Building with Classical Roots** sections of this book you will learn more about some of these Latin and Greek roots and about English words that derive from them. The lists that follow may help you figure out the meaning of new or unfamiliar words that you encounter in your reading.

Greek Root	Meaning	Sample Word
-astr-, -aster-, -astro-	star	astral, asteroid, astronaut
-auto-	self	autograph
-bio-	life	biography
-chron-, chrono-	time	chronic, chronological
-cosm-, -cosmo-	universe, order	microcosm, cosmopolitan
-cryph-, -crypt-	hidden, secret	apocryphal, cryptographer
-dem-, -demo-	people	epidemic, democracy
-dia-	through, across, between	diameter
-dog-, -dox-	opinion, teaching	dogmatic, orthodox
-gen-	race, kind, origin, birth	generation
-gnos-	know	diagnostic
-graph-, -graphy-, -gram-	write	graphite, autobiography, telegram
-log-, -logue-	speech, word, reasoning	logic, dialogue
-lys-	break down	analysis
-metr-, -meter-	measure	metric, kilometer
-micro-	small	microchip
-morph-	form, shape	amorphous
-naut-	sailor	cosmonaut
-phon-, -phone-, -phono-	sound, voice	phonics, telephone, phonograph
-pol-, -polis-	city, state	police, metropolis
-scop-, -scope-	watch, look at	telescopic, microscope
-tele-	far off, distant	television
-the-	put or place	parentheses

Latin Root	Meaning	Sample Word
-cap-, -capt-, -cept-, -cip-	take	capitulate, captive, concept, recipient
-cede-, -ceed-, -ceas-, -cess-	happen, yield, go	precede, proceed, decease, cessation
-cred-	believe	incredible
-dic-, -dict-	speak, say, tell	indicate, diction
-duc-, -duct-, -duit-	lead, conduct, draw	educate, conduct, conduit
-fac-, -fact-, -fect-, -fic-, -fy-	make	faculty, artifact, defect, beneficial, clarify
-ject-	throw	eject
-mis-, -miss-, -mit-, -mitt-	send	promise, missile, transmit, intermittent
-note-, -not-	know, recognize	denote, notion
-pel-, -puls-	drive	expel, compulsive
-pend-, -pens-	hang, weight, set aside	pendulum, pension
-pon-, -pos-	put, place	component, position
-port-	carry	portable
-rupt-	break	bankrupt
-scrib-, -scribe-, -script-	write	scribble, describe, inscription
-spec-, -spic-	look, see	spectator, conspicuous
-tac-, -tag-, -tang-, -teg-	touch	contact, contagious, tangible, integral
-tain-, -ten-, -tin-	hold, keep	contain, tenure, retinue
-temp-	time	tempo
-ven-, -vent-	come	intervene, convention
-vers-, -vert-	turn	reverse, invert
-voc-, -vok-	call	vocal, invoke

VOCABULARY AND READING

Word knowledge is essential to reading comprehension. Quite simply, the more words you know, the easier it is to make sense of what you read. Your growing knowledge of word meanings combined with an ability to read carefully and think about what you read will help you succeed in school and do well on standardized tests, including the new SAT, the ACT, and the PSAT.

The **Vocabulary for Comprehension** exercises in this book will give you the opportunity to put your vocabulary knowledge and critical reading skills to use. Each exercise consists of a nonfiction reading passage followed by comprehension questions. The passages and questions are similar to those that you are likely to find on standardized tests.

Kinds of Questions

The questions on the reading sections of standardized tests are formulated in many different ways, but they are usually only of a small number of kinds, or types— the same ones that appear most frequently in the Vocabulary for Comprehension exercises in this book.

Main Idea Questions generally ask what the passage as a whole is about. Questions about the main idea may begin like this:

- The primary or main purpose of the passage is
- The primary focus of the passage is on
- The passage is best described as
- The passage is primarily concerned with
- The title that best describes the content of the passage is

Often the main idea is stated in the first paragraph of the passage. Sometimes, however, the first paragraph serves as an introduction and the main idea is included later on. When you answer questions about the main idea, you should make sure that the answers you choose reflect the focus of the entire passage and not just part of it. You may also be asked the main idea of a specific paragraph.

Detail Questions focus on important information that is explicitly stated in the passage. Often, however, the correct answer choices do not use the exact language of the passage. They are instead restatements, or paraphrases, of the text. So, for example, the answer to a question about "trash production and disposal" might use the term "waste management."

Vocabulary-in-Context Questions check your ability to use context to identify a word's meaning. All vocabulary-in-context questions include line references so that you can refer back to the passage to see how and in what context the word is used.

Here are some examples:

- **Condone** (line 6) most nearly means
- **Eminent** (line 8) is best defined as
- The meaning of **diffuse** (line 30) is

It is important to use context to check your answer choices, particularly when the vocabulary word has more than one meaning. Among the choices may be two (or more) correct meanings of the word in question. Your task is to choose the meaning that best fits the context.

Inference Questions ask you to make inferences or draw conclusions from the passage. These questions often begin like this:

- It can be inferred from the passage that
- The author implies that
- The passage suggests that
- Evidently the author feels that

The inferences you make and the conclusions you draw must be based on the information in the passage. Your own knowledge and reasoning come into play in understanding what is implied and in reaching conclusions that are logical.

Questions about Tone show your understanding of the author's attitude toward the subject of the passage. Words that describe tone, or attitude, are "feeling" words, for example, *indifferent, ambivalent, scornful, astonished, respectful.* These are typical questions:

- The author's attitude toward . . . is best described as
- The author's perspective is that of . . .
- Which word best describes the author's tone . . .

To determine the tone, it's important to pay attention to the author's choice of words and note your personal reaction. The author's attitude may be positive *(respectful, astonished)*, negative *(scornful)*, or neutral *(indifferent, ambivalent).*

Questions about Author's Technique focus on the way a text is organized and the language the author uses. These questions ask you to think about structure and function. For example:

- The final paragraph serves to
- What is the function of the phrase . . . ?
- What does the author mean by . . . ?
- The author cites . . . in order to . . . .

To answer the questions, you must demonstrate an understanding of the way the author presents information and develops ideas.

Strategies

Here are some general strategies to help you in reading each passage and answering the questions.

- Read the introduction first. The introduction will provide a focus for the selection.

- Be an active reader. As you read, ask yourself questions about the passage, for example: What is this paragraph about? What does the writer mean here? Why does the writer include this information?

- Refer back to the passage when you answer the questions. In general, the order of the questions mirrors the organization of the passage, and many of the questions include paragraph or line references. It is often helpful to go back and reread before choosing an answer.

- Read carefully, and be sure to base your answer choices on the passage. There are answer choices that make sense, but are not based on the information in the passage. These may be true statements, but incorrect answers. The correct answers are either restatements of ideas in the text or inferences that can be made from the text.

- Consider each exercise a learning experience. Keep in mind that your ability to answer the questions correctly shows as much about your understanding of the questions as about your understanding of the passage.

GRAMMAR AND WRITING

In order to write well, so that your meaning and your purpose are clearly understood, you must use words correctly; but, more than that, you must also make sure that what you write is grammatically correct. Knowing the rules of grammar, usage, and mechanics—the conventions of standard English—make your writing not just correct but more powerful and persuasive, too.

As a student you are regularly challenged to write effectively and correctly not only in your English classes but in your social studies, science, and history classes, too. Furthermore, high schools and colleges have raised their expectations for graduates. If you have taken a standardized test recently or are preparing to take one, you know this only too well. The writing and grammar sections of these tests have grown more demanding than ever.

On these grammar sections, questions usually appear in one or two multiple-choice formats. In one, you must decide if a mistake has been made in a sentence and, if one has been made, identify it. In another format, you must decide if an identified word or phrase is incorrect and, if it is incorrect, choose from several options the best way to correct it.

The **Grammar in Context** exercise that appears in each of the five Reviews in this book will provide you with opportunity to review and apply grammar and usage rules that are critical to good writing and that are frequently tested on the multiple-choice parts of standardized tests. In Level H, these topics are:

• Misplaced modifiers

• Subject-verb agreement

• Faulty subordination

• Pronoun reference and shift

• Parallel construction

(For the sake of convenience, we sometimes use the term *grammar* to embrace all of the "rules" of English; but it's important to note that grammar, usage, and mechanics represent different aspects of writing. Grammar deals mostly with parts of speech and with parts of sentences and their relations. Usage, as the name suggests, concerns the way that words and phrases are used; usage topics would include, for example, irregular verbs, active and passive voice, subject-verb agreement, and double negatives. Mechanics deals with punctuation, capitalization, and spelling.)

There are many reasons to write and speak correctly other than to score well on standardized tests. You are judged by the way you write and speak. Your use of English is evaluated in the writing you do in school, on college applications, and in many different kinds of careers. You should be able to write and speak correctly when the situation calls for it—in a formal writing assignment, on a test, or in an interview. The more you practice standard English, the more comfortable and confident you will become when you write and speak.

WORKING WITH ANALOGIES

A verbal analogy expresses a relationship or comparison between sets of words. Normally, an analogy contains two pairs of words linked by a word or symbol that stands for an equals (=) sign. A complete analogy compares the two pairs of words and makes a statement about them. It asserts that the relationship between the first pair of words is the same as the relationship between the second pair.

In the **Analogies** exercises that appear in the Cumulative Reviews, you will be asked to complete analogies, that is, to choose the pair of words that best matches or parallels the relationship of the key, or given, pair of words. Here are two examples:

1. maple is to **tree** as
    a. acorn is to oak
    b. hen is to rooster
    c. rose is to flower
    d. shrub is to lilac

2. joyful is to **gloomy** as
    a. cheerful is to happy
    b. strong is to weak
    c. quick is to famous
    d. hungry is to starving

In order to find the correct answer to exercise 1, you must first determine the relationship between the two key words, **maple** and **tree**. In this case, that relationship might be expressed as "a maple is a kind (or type) of tree." The next step is to select from choices a, b, c, and d the pair of words that best reflects the same relationship. Clearly, the correct answer is (c); it is the only choice that parallels the relationship of the key words: a rose is a kind (or type) of flower, just as a maple is a kind (or type) of tree. The other choices do not express the same relationship.

In exercise 2, the relationship between the key words can be expressed as "joyful means the opposite of gloomy." Which of the choices best represents the same relationship? The answer, of course, is (b): "strong" means the opposite of "weak."

Here are examples of some other common analogy relationships:

Analogy	Key Relationship
big is to **large** as **little** is to **small**	**Big** means the same thing as **large**, just as **little** means the same thing as **small**.
brave is to **favorable** as **cowardly** is to **unfavorable**	The tone of **brave** is **favorable**, just as the tone of **cowardly** is **unfavorable**.
busybody is to **nosy** as **klutz** is to **clumsy**	A **busybody** is by definition someone who is **nosy**, just as a **klutz** is by definition someone who is **clumsy**.
cowardly is to **courage** as **awkward** is to **grace**	Someone who is **cowardly** lacks **courage**, just as someone who is **awkward** lacks **grace**.
visible is to **see** as **audible** is to **hear**	If something is **visible**, you can by definition **see** it, just as if something is **audible**, you can by definition **hear** it.
liar is to **truthful** as **bigot** is to **fair-minded**	A **liar** is by definition not likely to be **truthful**, just as a **bigot** is by definition not likely to be **fair-minded**.
eyes are to **see** as **ears** are to **hear**	You use your **eyes** to **see** with, just as you use your **ears** to **hear** with.

There are many different kinds of relationships represented in the analogy questions you will find in this book, but the key to solving any analogy is to find and express the relationship between the two key words.

This test contains a sampling of the words that are to be found in the exercises in this Level of VOCABULARY WORKSHOP. It will give you an idea of the types of words to be studied and their level of difficulty. When you have completed all the units, the Final Mastery Test at the end of this book will assess what you have learned. By comparing your results on the Final Mastery Test with your results on the Diagnostic Test below, you will be able to judge your progress.

Synonyms   *In each of the following groups, circle the word or phrase that **most nearly** expresses the meaning of the word in **boldface** type in the given phrase.*

1. an **ecumenical** conference
   a. financial   b. worldwide   c. moral   d. uninteresting

2. a **niggardly** allowance
   a. generous   b. lavish   c. adequate   d. stingy

3. **opt** to leave
   a. prepare   b. refuse   c. choose   d. fail

4. the **bane** of my life
   a. mainstay   b. joy   c. hobby   d. ruin

5. contributed **sub rosa** to the campaign
   a. covertly   b. legally   c. exceptionally   d. routinely

6. a **quizzical** look
   a. solemn   b. caustic   c. querulous   d. puzzled

7. find the **mot juste**
   a. perfect gift   b. right word   c. lost child   d. trouble spot

8. my **bête noire**
   a. nemesis   b. success   c. favorite   d. aspiration

9. an **insouciant** attitude
   a. serious   b. ambivalent   c. carefree   d. phlegmatic

10. a **noisome** atmosphere
   a. charming   b. noxious   c. loud   d. explosive

11. a **risible** development
   a. unexpected   b. fortunate   c. laughable   d. recent

12. **adjudicate** the dispute
   a. define   b. mediate   c. overhear   d. start

13. receive something as a **lagniappe**
   a. bonus   b. warning   c. visitor   d. honor

14. **gambol** on the green
   a. romp   b. lie   c. sleep   d. loiter

15. begin **in medias res**
   a. again   b. at the beginning   c. in the middle   d. at the conclusion

16. chimerical hopes
    a. buoyant   b. unrealistic   c. modest   d. achievable

17. a **touchstone** of valor
    a. medal   b. yardstick   c. champion   d. amulet

18. a **maudlin** story
    a. hilarious   b. terrifying   c. long   d. sentimental

19. condescend to see us
    a. refuse   b. stoop   c. attempt   d. plan

20. a terrible **faux pas**
    a. job   b. pain   c. loss   d. blunder

21. under the **aegis** of the university
    a. auspices   b. roof   c. solicitude   d. morass

22. an inadvertent **solecism**
    a. donnybrook   b. mistake   c. persiflage   d. fait accompli

23. an **affinity** for math
    a. jurisdiction   b. yearning   c. ignominy   d. penchant

24. strutted with **panache**
    a. flamboyance   b. lucubration   c. lagniappe   d. obloquy

25. always a fascinating **raconteur**
    a. aristocrat   b. mountebank   c. virtuoso   d. storyteller

26. steelworkers on their **precarious** perch
    a. perilous   b. sturdy   c. fervid   d. dank

27. no **vestige** of their culture
    a. liason   b. artifact   c. pastiche   d. harbinger

28. horrified by their **execrable** behavior
    a. insipid   b. pragmatic   c. reprehensible   d. picaresque

29. the ambassador's **unimpeachable** credentials
    a. pertinent   b. sullied   c. dubious   d. irrefutable

30. their **disparate** backgrounds
    a. questionable   b. dissimilar   c. irrelevant   d. similar

Antonyms

*In each of the following groups, circle the word that is **most nearly opposite** in meaning to the word in **boldface** type in the given phrase.*

31. quixotic schemes
    a. fanciful   b. extravagant   c. realistic   d. visionary

32. a **lackluster** performance
    a. early   b. dazzling   c. exhausting   d. mediocre

33. an **apocryphal** story
    a. authentic   b. fictitious   c. romantic   d. sordid

34. a **mellifluous** voice
    a. sweet   b. unusual   c. low   d. shrill

35. an inexplicable sense of **euphoria**
   a. happiness   b. drowsiness   c. contentment   d. melancholy

36. a **diaphanous** curtain
   a. opaque   b. flimsy   c. colorful   d. full

37. minuscule amounts
   a. small   b. huge   c. unknown   d. profitable

38. a **viable** arrangement
   a. attractive   b. impracticable   c. reasonable   d. dangerous

39. a **gargantuan** appetite
   a. depraved   b. tiny   c. stimulated   d. immense

40. deliver a lengthy **philippic**
   a. panegyric   b. diatribe   c. harangue   d. invective

41. an **ineluctable** conclusion
   a. tragic   b. decisive   c. avoidable   d. peaceful

42. constrict the flow
   a. control   b. end   c. inspect   d. enlarge

43. a **waggish** fellow
   a. mature   b. childish   c. unbalanced   d. dour

44. a **malleable** mind
   a. costly   b. indestructible   c. intractable   d. brilliant

45. apropos of our discussion
   a. irrelevant to   b. needed for   c. germane to   d. stemming from

46. a **hidebound** view
   a. liberal   b. epic   c. ribald   d. narrow-minded

47. an **ancillary** role
   a. auxiliary   b. indigenous   c. principal   d. pessimistic

48. the critic's **bilious** review
   a. ludicrous   b. benevolent   c. cowardly   d. delightful

49. a member of the **hoi polloi**
   a. mumbo jumbo   b. faux pas   c. upper class   d. derring-do

50. speak to the **contumacious** students
   a. cooperative   b. unruly   c. bored   d. ineluctable

Definitions

Note carefully the spelling, pronunciation, part(s) of speech, and definition(s) of each of the following words. Then write the word in the blank space(s) in the illustrative sentence(s) following. Finally, study the lists of synonyms and antonyms given at the end of each entry.

1. adjunct
(aj′ ənkt)

(*n.*) something added to something else as helpful or useful but not essential; an assistant or helper; a valuable quality or characteristic; (*adj.*) added or connected in a subordinate capacity; attached to a faculty or staff in an auxiliary capacity

The test manual was an _____ provided free with purchases of the new textbook series.

An _____ art professor will be hired.

SYNONYMS: (*n.*) associate, addition, accessory

2. bellwether
(bel′ weth ər)

(*n.*) the male sheep that leads the flock to the slaughterhouse; a leader, as in a desperate or violent undertaking; an indicator of trends

When their _____ was captured, the mob disbanded.

SYNONYMS: ringleader, initiator, barometer
ANTONYMS: follower, imitator, emulator

3. caterwaul
(kat′ ər wôl)

(*v.*) to howl or screech like a cat; to quarrel; (*n.*) a harsh or noisy cry; a racket

The desperate survivors _____ about their suffering.

The _____ in the alley kept us awake.

SYNONYMS: (*v.*) whine; (*n.*) wail, screech

4. chimerical
(ki mer′ i kəl)

(*adj.*) absurd; wildly fantastic; impossible

They proposed yet another _____ get-rich-quick scheme.

SYNONYMS: fanciful, visionary, quixotic, pie-in-the-sky
ANTONYMS: realistic, down-to-earth, practicable

5. effete
(i fēt′)

(adj.) lacking in wholesome vigor or energy; worn-out or exhausted; sterile or unable to produce; out-of-date

The _____ society was once a thriving and vigorous one.

SYNONYMS: decadent, enfeebled, outmoded
ANTONYMS: thriving, burgeoning, vigorous, dynamic

6. fait accompli
(fe ta kôm plē′)

(*n.*) an accomplished and presumably irreversible deed, fact, or action

The proud generals confidently declared the fall of the
rebel stronghold a _____.
SYNONYM: accomplished fact

7. hidebound
(hīd′ baûnd)

(*adj.*) narrow-minded and rigid, especially in opinions or
prejudices;stubbornly and unthinkingly conservative

The _____ administrator stood by
the outdated ways of previous administrations.
SYNONYMS: intolerant, inflexible
ANTONYMS: open-minded, tolerant, liberal, progressive

8. hierarchy
(hi′ ə rär kē)

(*n.*) any system of things or people arranged or graded one
above another in order of rank, wealth, class, etc.

Within the governmental _____, the
voice of the junior senator was not a powerful one.
SYNONYMS: chain of command, pecking order

9. liturgy
(lit′ ər jē)

(*n.*) a religious service or rite; the form of a ritual or other act of
public worship

The _____ has been modernized.
SYNONYMS: ceremony, observance

10. mirage
(mi räzh′)

(*n.*) something illusory, without substance, or without a basis in
reality; an illusion

Deceived by a _____, the desert
travelers perked up at the thought of water and shade.
SYNONYM: optical illusion

11. morass
(mə ras′)

(*n.*) a patch of low, soft, wet ground; a swamp; a confusing
situation in which one is entrapped, as in quicksand

After several bad performances, the aging athlete wallowed
in a _____ of self doubt.
SYNONYMS: bog, quagmire
ANTONYMS: solid ground, bedrock, terra firma

12. noisome
(noi′ səm)

(*adj.*) offensive or disgusting; foul-smelling; harmful or injurious

The _____ atmosphere of the
slaughterhouse overwhelmed the visitors.
SYNONYMS: fetid, noxious, vile, loathsome
ANTONYMS: wholesome, pleasant, sweet-smelling

13. oblivious
(ə bliv′ ē əs)

(*adj.*) forgetful; unaware

The climbers were totally _____ of
the dangers ahead.
SYNONYM: insensible
ANTONYMS: aware, mindful, cognizant, alert

14. poltroon
(pol trün′)

(*n.*) a base coward

The _____ was caught in the act of deserting.

SYNONYMS: craven, dastard, "chicken"
ANTONYMS: hero, stalwart, gallant

15. proselyte
(pros′ ə līt)

(*n.*) a convert; a disciple

A group of zealous _____ demonstrated in the square.

SYNONYMS: novice, neophyte
ANTONYMS: master, teacher, guide, guru

16. quasi
(kwā′ zī) *or*
(kwä′ zē)

(*adj.*) resembling but not actually being; seemingly but not actually or completely

They formed a _____ partnership.

SYNONYMS: kind of, semi-, as if
ANTONYMS: totally, completely, actually, in fact

17. raillery
(rā′ lər ē)

(*n.*) good-humored ridicule; teasing

The good-natured _____ in the locker room pleased the coach.

SYNONYMS: banter, persiflage

18. ribald
(rib′ əld)

(*adj.*) irreverently mocking; coarse, vulgar, or indecent in language

The actor tells _____ stories about life in the theater world.

SYNONYMS: bawdy, risqué
ANTONYMS: seemly, proper, decorous

19. supine
(sù pīn′)

(*adj.*) lying flat on one's back; listless or lethargic; apathetic or passive

The hiker relaxed in a _____ position.

SYNONYMS: prone, prostrate; inert
ANTONYMS: upright, erect, perpendicular, vertical

20. vignette
(vin yet′)

(*n.*) a short description or sketch; a picture or illustration with edges that gradually shade off; a decorative design on the title page of a book or at the beginning or end of a chapter

All enjoyed the writer's _____ of country life.

SYNONYMS: thumbnail sketch, anecdote
ANTONYMS: epic, full-length treatment

Completing the Sentence

From the words for this unit, choose the one that best completes each of the following sentences. Write the word in the space provided.

1. If you think that the literature of earlier ages was always staid and proper, take a look at some of the _____ stories in the *Decameron*, written more than 600 years ago.

2. Failure in itself is no disgrace, but the _____ acceptance of failure certainly is.

3. Taking advantage of the young man's naïve idealism, they sought to make him a(n) _____ to serve in their wild revolutionary plots.

4. Their youthful enthusiasm for literature had degenerated over the years into a(n) _____ preoccupation with quibbling criticism and minor details.

5. I detected an undertone of hostility and ridicule in the remarks, which were ostensibly no more than good-natured _____.

6. The local Parents' Association has on many occasions served as a willing _____ to the administration and staff of our school.

7. Since the Smithsonian Institution is only partly under the control of the United States government, it is considered a(n) _____ governmental institution.

8. The newspaper published a series of charming _____ by my Aunt Alice—brief sketches of the town she grew up in.

9. I regret Fred's resignation as much as anyone, but I think that we must regard it as a(n) _____ and find someone to take his place.

10. I think that the critic was a little harsh when he observed that the band's lead vocalist did not sing so much as _____.

11. A handful of self-appointed "leaders" served as the _____ who induced the mob to surge through the barriers.

12. Cynics may say that the goal of universal and lasting peace is no more than a(n) _____, but we must continue to hope and strive for it.

13. As late as the seventeenth century, researchers called "alchemists" devoted their lives to the pursuit of _____ schemes for turning iron into gold.

14. She used talent, charm, energy, and determination to fight her way up the corporate _____ until she attained the highest position in the company.

15. Don Quixote dismissed as a mere _____ anyone who refused to join in his crusade against the forces of evil.

16. Polluted by the spill from a nearby chemical plant, the once beautiful lake had become a foul pool, _____ and hideous.

17. Advocates of equal rights maintain that we must reject the _____ prejudices that bar the physically impaired from many occupations.

18. The use of English rather than traditional languages in religious ceremonies is evidence of efforts to modernize and revitalize the _____ of various denominations.

19. Ever since she learned of the failure of her project, she has been mired in a(n) _____ of disappointment and self-recrimination.

20. As a rule, I am not a particularly proud or combative person, but I cannot be _____ to the fact that you have deliberately insulted me.

Synonyms

*Choose the word from this unit that is **the same** or **most nearly the same** in meaning as the **boldface** word or expression in the given phrase. Write the word on the line provided.*

1. brought another **neophyte** into the fold _____

2. a **thumbnail sketch** of urban life _____

3. has a **fanciful** notion of what the future holds _____

4. found themselves in a **quagmire** _____

5. a steady stream of **banter** _____

6. entranced by the **optical illusion** _____

7. angered by the **outmoded** views of the leader _____

8. startled by the sudden **wail** _____

9. embarrassed by the **bawdy** prose _____

10. tempted by the idea of **semi**-retirement _____

11. recognized the **irreversible situation** _____

12. unfamiliar with the **ceremony** _____

13. at the pinnacle of the **pecking order** _____

14. an **associate** hired for the summer _____

15. hasty instructions from the **ringleader** _____

Antonyms

*Choose the word from this unit that is **most nearly opposite** in meaning to the **boldface** word or expression in the given phrase. Write the word on the line provided.*

16. known as a **progressive** thinker _____

17. nauseated by the **pleasant** odor _____

18. seemed **mindful** of the chaos all around _____

19. placed in a **perpendicular** position _____

20. enjoyed a deserved reputation as a **hero** _____

*Circle the **boldface** word that more satisfactorily completes each of the following sentences.*

1. Overly sensitive to any suggestion of ridicule, young Rogers seemed to be hurt even by a friend's good-natured (**raillery, proselytes**).

2. The lyrics of the song, presented as though they were devastating wit, were in my opinion no more than a course and (**supine, ribald**) jest.

3. They have confronted us not with a theoretical possibility but with a(n) (**adjunct, fait accompli**); now we must decide what we can do about it.

4. With penetrating insight and a marvelous ear for dialogue, the author gave us in a few words an unforgettable (**adjunct, vignette**) of a confused but hopeful adolescent.

5. After a brief period of popularity, their cheap and vulgar novels lost their appeal and sank into well-deserved (**proselyte, oblivion**).

6. Failure to stand up for your rights is not being "prudent" or "moderate"; it is the behavior of a (**poltroon, bellwether**).

7. Although the old Senator no longer holds any public office, her fame and prestige are so great that she is still regarded as a (**quasi, hidebound**) public figure.

8. Martin Luther King, Jr. appealed to his countrymen to abandon the (**noisome, hidebound**) stereotypes of racism and rise to a new level of understanding.

9. Financial analysts carefully watch the performance of certain stocks, which they regard as (**bellwethers, mirages**) for indications of economic trends.

10. How can you expect a prompt response from an agency that is bogged down in a veritable (**morass, liturgy**) of unnecessary red tape?

11. By late imperial times, centuries of soft living had turned the once hardy Romans into an (**oblivious, effete**) and indolent people.

12. We have lived to see the acceptance and enactment of reform programs that, when first proposed, were dismissed as absolutely (**chimerical, oblivious**).

13. The great historian Edward Gibbon sought to explain how and why the (**proselytizing, liturgical**) efforts of the early Christian church met with such extraordinary success.

14. As I listened to the talk of those unlettered folk, suffused with love and reverence, I felt that their simple words were a (**raillery, liturgy**) worthy of respect.

15. A superintendent is at the head of the (**hierarchy, vignette**) of educators responsible for the schooling of our children and young people.

16. I am willing to listen to any reasonable grievances you may have, but this constant (**caterwauling, hierarchy**) about trivia has exhausted my patience.

17. He is so (**ribald, hidebound**) in his political views that he won't even listen to opinions that differ from his own.

18. Her unfailing courtesy to others is not a mere (**adjunct, morass**) of her personality; it reflects the essential values and standards by which she lives.

19. Almost incredibly, a formidable resistance movement had been organized by people whom we had always associated with (**supine, noisome**) submission to authority.

20. Your serene confidence that "everything will come out all right in the end" may be reassuring, but it is no more than a (**morass, mirage**).

Read the following passage, in which some of the words you have studied in this unit appear in **boldface** type. Then complete each statement given below the passage by circling the letter of the item that is **the same** or **almost the same** in meaning as the highlighted word.

Before There Were Movies

(Line)

From the 1880s to the 1930s, the most popular form of entertainment in the United States was vaudeville. The roots of vaudeville, a French term for an amusing play with music, lay in the **ribald** variety shows popular in mid-nineteenth-century saloons. The purpose of these shows was to attract men who would spend money in the saloon.

(5) One of the first important vaudeville producers, B. F. Keith, sought to expand the audience to include women and children. To do so, he imposed upon his performers strict rules forbidding vulgarity and hired the best talent he could find in Europe as well as the United States.

(10) The results were phenomenal. Gone were the **noisome** antics of the saloon performances. Within twenty-five years, nearly 1,000 vaudeville theaters across the country filled up with two million spectators each day.

(15) Audiences saw jugglers, singers, and comedians, as well as **vignettes** both humorous and dramatic. A typical show included from eight to ten acts. Comedians Jack Benny, George Burns, and W. C.

(20) Fields were among the stars.

The advent of motion pictures brought doom to vaudeville. To the enthusiasts of the new medium, vaudeville must have seemed an **effete** entertainment, one that had seen its

Vaudeville comics tickled audiences' funny bones with slapstick skits and zany jokes.

(25) day. Vaudeville producers tried to hold onto their dwindling audiences by showing motion pictures between acts. It didn't work. People flocked to the movies instead.

The old vaudeville stars are gone, but their legacy remains. Today, a new generation of vaudevillians has recreated the **chimerical** world of juggling, acrobatics, mime, silly skits, and eye-popping sight gags. Knee-slapping corny jokes

(30) are back and so are magic tricks, sword swallowing, and animal acts. Audiences have returned, and entertainment for the whole family is back on center stage.

---

1. The meaning of **ribald** (line 3) is
   a. apathetic   c. bawdy
   b. rich   d. intolerant

2. Noisome (line 11) most nearly means
   a. auxiliary   c. fanciful
   b. insensible   d. offensive

3. Vignettes (line 16) is best defined as
   a. sketches   c. quagmires
   b. performers   d. illusions

4. The meaning of **effete** (line 24) is
   a. visionary   c. outmoded
   b. inflexible   d. decorous

5. Chimerical (line 28) most nearly means
   a. vigorous   c. cognizant
   b. quixotic   d. proper

Definitions

Note carefully the spelling, pronunciation, part(s) of speech, and definition(s) of each of the following words. Then write the word in the blank space(s) in the illustrative sentence(s) following. Finally, study the lists of synonyms and antonyms given at the end of each entry.

1. aegis
(ē' jis)

(*n.*) protection; patronage; sponsorship

The arts and education programs of the United Nations are under the _____ of UNESCO.

SYNONYM: auspices

2. apprise
(ə prīz')

(*v.*) to inform of; to make aware of by giving oral or written notice

The spokesperson will _____ us of the latest developments.

SYNONYMS: acquaint, notify
ANTONYMS: keep secret, withhold information

3. bibulous
(bib' yə ləs)

(*adj.*) fond of or inclined to drink; absorbent

The retired sailor was a _____ old codger.

SYNONYMS: inebrious, alcoholic
ANTONYMS: teetotaling, abstemious, temperate

4. claque
(klak)

(*n.*) a group of people hired to applaud a performer or performance; enthusiastic or fawning admirers; an opera hat

The soprano's _____ was in attendance, as usual.

SYNONYMS: fan club, flatterers, hangers-on

5. deracinate
(di ras' ə nāt)

(*v.*) to pull up by the roots; to root out, uproot, or dislocate; to eliminate all traces of

One way to _____ prejudice from our society is to heighten public awareness.

SYNONYMS: extirpate, eradicate, expunge
ANTONYMS: implant, nurture, foster, instill

6. eleemosynary
(el i mos' ə ner ē)

(*adj.*) charitable; dependent upon or supported by charity; derived from or provided by charity

Some _____ institutions use phone solicitations to obtain contributions.

SYNONYMS: philanthropic, beneficent
ANTONYMS: selfish, self-seeking, uncharitable

7. indigenous
(in dij' ə nəs)

(*adj.*) originating in the country or region where found, native; inborn; inherent

Grizzly bears and mountain lions are two examples of wildlife _____ to the Rockies.

SYNONYMS: endemic, domestic, homegrown
ANTONYMS: foreign, alien, exoteric, imported

8. lachrymose
(lak' rə mōs)

(*adj.*) given to tears or weeping; causing to shed tears; mournful, lugubrious

It was a _____ tale of poverty and woe.

SYNONYMS: tearful, doleful, dolorous
ANTONYMS: dry-eyed, cheerful, merry, hilarious

9. lexicon
(lek' sə kən)

(*n.*) a dictionary of a language; the special vocabulary of a person, group, or subject; a compendium

The _____ of computer technology is large and growing.

SYNONYMS: wordbook, glossary

10. melee
(mā' lā)

(*n.*) a confused struggle; a violent free-for-all; a tumultuous mingling

Many fans were hurt in the _____ that followed the soccer match.

SYNONYMS: fracas, brawl, scuffle, donnybrook
ANTONYMS: friendly chat, peace and quiet

11. microcosm
(mī' krə kos əm)

(*n.*) a miniature world or universe; a group or system viewed as the model of a larger group or system

The ocean liner is a _____ of society in the novel *Ship of Fools*.

SYNONYMS: epitome, world in little
ANTONYMS: universe, macrocosm, cosmos, totality

12. minuscule
(min' əs kyül)

(*adj.*) very small, tiny; (*n.*) a lowercase letter

I ate only a _____ portion of the dessert.

In the typeface that the poet chose, every letter used in the poem is a _____.

SYNONYMS: (*adj.*) infinitesimal, insignificant
ANTONYMS: (*adj.*) huge, massive, monumental

13. obfuscate
(ob' fə skāt)

(*v.*) to darken or obscure; to confuse or bewilder

The pedantic lecturer's long-winded explanation served only to _____ the meaning of the thesis.

SYNONYM: muddy the waters
ANTONYMS: clarify, elucidate, explicate

14. paternalism
(pə tûr' nə liz əm)

(*n.*) the policy or practice of treating or governing people in the manner of a father dealing with his children

The President won over the worried populace with his attitude of kind _____.

SYNONYMS: benevolence, solicitude, fatherliness

15. polarize
(pō' lə rīz)

(*v.*) to cause to concentrate around two conflicting or contrasting positions; to cause light to vibrate in a pattern

The debate served to _____ public opinion on the issue.

SYNONYMS: split, divide, alienate, estrange
ANTONYMS: unite, unify, reconcile

16. purview
(pər' vyü)

(*n.*) the range, extent, or scope of something; in law, the scope or limit of what is provided in a statute

The subject was outside the _____ of the mayor's authority.

SYNONYMS: jurisdiction, orbit

17. sanguine
(saŋ' gwin)

(*adj.*) having a ruddy complexion; of a naturally cheerful, confident, or optimistic outlook

Scientists remain _____ about the chances of finding a cure for the deadly disease.

SYNONYMS: flushed, rosy
ANTONYMS: bloodless, ashen, pessimistic, gloomy

18. solecism
(sol' ə siz əm)

(*n.*) a substandard or ungrammatical usage; a breach of etiquette; any impropriety or mistake

One common _____ is "irregardless."

SYNONYMS: misusage, blunder, faux pas
ANTONYM: correct usage

19. vassal
(vas' el)

(*n.*) a person under the protection of a feudal lord to whom he or she owes allegiance; a subordinate or dependent; a servant; (*adj.*) subservient

The duke's _____ was forced to fight for the king, to whom the duke owed allegiance.

As a _____ nation, India provided troops for British armies.

SYNONYMS: (*n.*) menial, minion; (*adj.*) servile
ANTONYM: (*n.*) overlord

20. verisimilitude
(ver ə si mil' ə tüd)

(*n.*) the quality of appearing to be true, real, likely, or probable

The play's _____ won praise from critics.

SYNONYMS: realism, lifelikeness, authenticity

Completing the Sentence

From the words for this unit, choose the one that best completes each of the following sentences. Write the word in the space provided.

1. I am not given to undue optimism, but the preliminary results of the polls make me _____ about the outcome of the election.

2. A hard-line speech may gain her the applause of her followers, but overall it will _____ sentiments throughout the country and impair national unity.

3. Is the expression "It is me" to be regarded as a(n) _____ or as an acceptable idiomatic form?

4. He came to realize that the inner city in which he had been raised was a(n) _____ of the sufferings of poor people all over the world.

5. She defended her policy of hiring a(n) _____ by noting that even with a supportive audience, someone is needed to get the applause started.

6. The third period was marred by a bench-clearing _____ that left the hockey rink littered with discarded gloves and sticks.

7. A case of that type, which does not involve a Federal law or constitutional issue, does not come within the _____ of the Supreme Court.

8. "The rash and _____ behavior of that young hothead almost cost us the battle, to say nothing of the war," the general remarked sourly.

9. Without expressing opinions, simply _____ us as promptly as possible of the results of the conference.

10. No matter how fantastic and far-fetched the themes of Ray Bradbury's stories may be, he seems able to achieve an extraordinary effect of _____ .

11. Both sides let on that the negotiators were still miles apart, when in fact the distance that separated them was _____ .

12. Only within recent years has a complete _____ of the Latin language been compiled.

13. The issue is basically a simple one, and your efforts to _____ it by raising endless technical objections will have no effect on us.

14. It is easy to be cynical about the motives that lie behind their _____ activities, but I truly believe that they want to help people.

15. Surprisingly, the white potato, which I have always associated with Ireland, is _____ to the Americas.

16. _____ from their Old World environments, European immigrants had difficult adjustments to make.

17. The people of this impoverished area need a program that will "help them to help themselves"—not a form of _____ that will make them completely dependent on outside aid.

18. If you are ever to get out of this tangled mess, now is the time for action, not indulgence in _____ self-pity.

19. When South Korea was invaded, the United States organized a collective defense effort under the _____ of the United Nations.

20. At the outset of World War II, Lithuania lost its sovereignty and became an unwilling _____ of the Soviet Union.

Synonyms

*Choose the word from this unit that is **the same** or **most nearly the same** in meaning as the **boldface** word or expression in the given phrase. Write the word on the line provided.*

1. acknowledged for its **authenticity** _____

2. under the **auspices** of the church _____

3. left early and missed the **donnybrook** _____

4. within the **jurisdiction** of the sheriff _____

5. neglected to **notify** the townspeople _____

6. a small, private, **philanthropic** organization _____

7. the **hangers-on** waiting by the stage door _____

8. using the programmers' **special vocabulary** _____

9. a **menial** in the royal family's service _____

10. to **divide** voters' sympathies _____

11. **native** to the region _____

12. hopes to **expunge** the bad blood _____

13. commits a **faux pas** at every turn _____

14. the **benevolence** of the dictator _____

15. a **model** of the entire park _____

Antonyms

*Choose the word from this unit that is **most nearly opposite** in meaning to the **boldface** word or expression in the given phrase. Write the word on the line provided.*

16. sought to **clarify** my view of the event _____

17. **pessimistic** about the test results _____

18. invited all their **teetotaling** relatives _____

19. in the **cheerful** moment that followed _____

20. had a **monumental** effect on the crowd _____

Choosing the Right Word

*Circle the **boldface** word that more satisfactorily completes each of the following sentences.*

1. Their standards are so rigid and so devoid of a sense of proportion that they elevate every minor (**lexicon, solecism**) to the level of a major crime.

2. Falstaff, as conceived by Shakespeare, is not just a (**lachrymose, bibulous**) old braggart but an archetype of human appetites and joy in living.

3. Is it any wonder that the young quarterback is getting a swelled head when he seems always to be surrounded by a(n) (**claque, aegis**) of fawning admirers?

4. It is not enough merely to push aside our prejudices and pretend they don't exist; we must (**deracinate, apprise**) these evils from our minds and personalities.

5. From the observatory atop the Empire State Building, the pedestrians on the streets below look as (**sanguine, minuscule**) as ants.

6. Even the public opinion polls, which showed a strong trend toward our candidate, did not make us overly (**indigenous, sanguine**) about our chances of winning.

7. Those later scenes, in the opinion of many critics, had so much self-conscious pathos that they lacked conviction and (**verisimilitude, microcosm**).

8. For many years, there was a tendency among Americans and Europeans to ignore the highly developed (**eleemosynary, indigenous**) cultures of the peoples of Africa.

9. Compared to today's free agents, the ballplayers of yesteryear were practically the (**lexicon, vassals**) of the team owners.

10. A basketball team will be sent to the Far East under the (**claque, aegis**) of the State Department to play native teams in various countries.

11. I think it was very inconsiderate of her to wait until this late date before she (**apprised, obfuscated**) us of her intention to quit the class show.

12. In spite of the development of social security and insurance plans by the government, there is still a need for private (**minuscule, eleemosynary**) institutions to provide special services for needy people.

13. If we disregard the emotions and desires of other groups in our area, we are simply going to increase partisanship and (**deracinate, polarize**) the whole community.

14. The movie started off well, but the later scenes, with the beautiful young heroine slowly dying of cancer, became overwrought and (**bibulous, lachrymose**).

15. In the tragedy that overtakes the pathetic Lennie in *Of Mice and Men*, we see in (**microcosm, purview**) the cruelty and injustice that pervade our society.

16. Please do not try to (**apprise, obfuscate**) your responsibility in this matter by irrelevant criticisms of other people's behavior.

17. I came to resent the company's (**solecism, paternalism**) because it assumed that employees lacked the self-reliance to take care of themselves.

18. Under the American system of personal liberty, there are many aspects of daily life that are not within the (**claque, purview**) of any governmental authority.

19. Morality is not a criterion that can be used to judge whether or not a word belongs in a (**microcosm, lexicon**) of the language in which it is used.

20. At rush hour, I always have a hard time fighting my way through the (**melee, claque**) of tired commuters scurrying through the station.

Read the following passage, in which some of the words you have studied in this unit appear in **boldface** type. Then complete each statement given below the passage by circling the letter of the item that is **the same** or **almost the same** in meaning as the highlighted word.

Noah's Mark

(Line)

In his lifetime, Noah Webster compiled and published two major works that irrevocably distinguished the English spoken in the United States from that spoken in Great Britain. These works eloquently expressed their author's **sanguine** conviction that the citizens of the burgeoning United States ought to express themselves in an idiom as unique and rich as their young nation's spirit. (5)

The first of the two, *A Grammatical Institute of the English Language,* was published in 1783, when Webster was twenty-five years old. The "Blue-Backed Speller," so nicknamed for its blue cover, quickly replaced the British textbooks then in use. Within the author's **purview** was no less than the creation of a uniform American-English language, with American (10) words and American spellings. Webster sought to simplify spellings in order to differentiate them from those in British dictionaries. *Musick* became *music. Colour* became *color.* Such changes in spelling became the American (15) standard.

The word for this animal first appeared in Webster's 1828 dictionary.

During its one hundred years of use, Webster's book eradicated many distinctions between different provincial colonial dialects. It became one of the most popular books of its time, with (20) sales second only to those of the Bible.

In 1828, after laboring for nearly thirty years, Webster published his masterpiece, the first comprehensive **lexicon** of American English. *An American Dictionary of the English Language* contained 70,000 entries and (25) was published in two volumes. In addition to revising spellings and pronunciations to reflect national practice, Webster included a number of words **indigenous** to North America. So it was that the words *hickory*, *skunk*, *squash*, and others made their first appearance in a dictionary.

Sales of Webster's highly praised but expensively priced dictionary were (30) lackluster. When Charles and George Merriam acquired the rights to publish new editions, they lowered the price—a sound business decision. Sales of the first Merriam-Webster dictionary boomed.

---

1. The meaning of **sanguine** (line 3) is
   a. abandoned   c. confident
   b. recovered   d. closed

2. The meaning of **purview** (line 9) is
   a. sponsorship   c. fan club
   b. scope   d. struggle

3. Lexicon (line 24) most nearly means
   a. orbit   c. model
   b. clarification   d. wordbook

4. Indigenous (line 27) most nearly means
   a. native   c. doleful
   b. given   d. paternal

Definitions

Note carefully the spelling, pronunciation, part(s) of speech, and definition(s) of each of the following words. Then write the word in the blank space(s) in the illustrative sentence(s) following. Finally, study the lists of synonyms and antonyms given at the end of each entry.

1. ancillary
(an' sə ler ē)

(*adj.*) subordinate or supplementary

The aide serves in an _____ position.

SYNONYMS: auxiliary, subsidiary, accessory
ANTONYMS: central, key, primary, principal, main

2. bowdlerize
(bōd' lə rīz)

(*v.*) to remove material considered offensive (from a book, play, film, etc.)

The writers refused to _____ the book when they turned it into a screenplay.

SYNONYMS: censor, purge, expurgate

3. condescend
(kon di send')

(*v.*) to come down or stoop voluntarily to a lower level; to deal with people in a patronizing manner

The fashion designer _____ to speak to reporters.

SYNONYM: deign

4. cozen
(kəz' ən)

(*v.*) to trick; to cheat or swindle

Some taxi drivers _____ unsuspecting tourists.

SYNONYMS: dupe, deceive, beguile, inveigle

5. enclave
(en' klāv)

(*n.*) an enclosed district, region, or area inhabited by a particular group of people or having a special character

The mountains afforded the displaced townspeople and the local militia an _____ of resistance.

SYNONYMS: island, subgroup

6. forte
(fôrt) *or* (fôr' tā)

(*n.*) a person's strong point; what a person does best

Although I love listening to piano music, playing the instrument is not my _____.

SYNONYMS: gift, aptitude, specialty
ANTONYMS: weakness, shortcoming, foible

7. gratis
(gra′ tis)

(*adj.*) free; (*adv.*) without charge

The food provided was _____.

During the filming, a local restaurant provided meals to the crew _____.

SYNONYMS: (*adj.*) on the house; (*adv.*) freely
ANTONYM: (*adv.*) for a price

8. icon
(ī′ kän)

(*n.*) a representation or image of a sacred personage, often considered sacred itself; an image or picture; a symbol; a graphic symbol on a computer monitor display; an object of blind devotion

The museum's exhibit of _____ included several from Czarist Russia.

SYNONYMS: emblem, idol

9. interstice
(in tər′ stis)

(*n.*) a small, narrow space between things or parts of things

Once it slipped through the _____ in the fence, the rabbit headed straight for the vegetables.

SYNONYMS: gap, slot, crevice, interval, lacuna

10. macrocosm
(mak′ rō koz əm)

(*n.*) the universe considered as a whole; the entire complex structure of something

During the course of their college education, many students study the economic _____.

SYNONYMS: cosmos, entirety
ANTONYMS: model, miniature, microcosm

11. mountebank
(maun′ tə baŋk)

(*n.*) a trickster or swindler; a charlatan

The _____ who sold surefire remedies for every imaginable ailment was finally exposed.

SYNONYMS: impostor, quack
ANTONYMS: sucker, dupe, "mark," "pigeon"

12. paean
(pē′ ən)

(*n.*) a song of praise, joy, or triumph

The audience responded with a _____ of exultation when the ceremony ended.

SYNONYMS: hymn, ode, anthem
ANTONYMS: dirge, elegy, lament, threnody

13. persiflage
(pər′ sə fläzh)

(*n.*) lighthearted joking, talk, or writing

The friends engaged in _____ from the moment their reunion began until the last of them left.

SYNONYMS: banter, jesting, repartee, badinage

14. plethora
(pleth' ə rə)

(*n.*) overfullness; superabundance; superfluity

The inquisitive journalists besieged the harried celebrity with a _____ of personal questions.

SYNONYMS: surplus, surfeit, glut, excess
ANTONYMS: shortage, paucity, dearth, scarcity

15. pragmatic
(prag mat' ik)

(*adj.*) concerned with practical considerations or values; dealing with actions and results rather than with abstract theory; stiff in one's opinions

The mayor takes a _____ approach to the city's problems.

SYNONYMS: down-to-earth, businesslike
ANTONYMS: idealistic, impractical, visionary

16. quizzical
(kwiz' i kəl)

(*adj.*) puzzled; mocking; odd; equivocal

The politician's unexpected comment left all who heard it with _____ expressions on their faces.

SYNONYMS: peculiar, perplexed, mystified, derisive
ANTONYMS: unequivocal, crystal-clear, unambiguous

17. rapacity
(rə pas' ə tē)

(*n.*) inordinate greed; the disposition to obtain one's desires by force, extortion, or plunder

With the _____ of a shark, the ruthless new company went after its competitors' clients.

SYNONYMS: avarice, cupidity, voraciousness
ANTONYMS: liberality, generosity, altruism

18. schism
(siz' əm) *or*
(skiz' əm)

(*n.*) a formal split within a religious organization; any division or separation of a group or organization into hostile factions

What began as a disagreement over a minor issue led to a bitter _____ within the party.

SYNONYMS: rift, breach
ANTONYMS: united front, reconciliation

19. therapeutic
(ther ə pyü' tik)

(*adj.*) having the power to heal or cure; beneficial

Many believe in the _____ effects attributed to the waters of natural hot springs.

SYNONYMS: curative, salutary, salubrious
ANTONYMS: harmful, injurious, deleterious

20. virtuoso
(vər chü ō' sō)

(*n.*) a brilliant performer; a person with masterly skill or technique; (*adj.*) masterly or brilliant

Franz Liszt was a piano _____.

I was treated to a _____ performance.

SYNONYMS: (*n.*) expert, master, prodigy, maestro
ANTONYMS: (*n.*) amateur, beginner, novice; (*adj.*) mediocre

Completing the Sentence

From the words for this unit, choose the one that best completes each of the following sentences. Write the word in the space provided.

1. Playing on his vanity and his desire to be known as a "good guy," I tried to _____ him into lending me his car.

2. To promote circulation, the publisher offered to throw in home delivery _____ for new subscribers to the Sunday edition.

3. She thought of herself as a combination of Mark Twain and H. L. Mencken, but her attempts at "devastating _____" were not very funny.

4. In attempting to make the novel acceptable to the general public, the editor so _____ it that it lost its quality of stark realism.

5. His self-importance stems from his inability to appreciate the very minor part he plays in the _____ of human affairs.

6. His exaggerated claims for an expensive painkiller that turned out to be no more than aspirin exposed him as a(n) _____.

7. He considers himself such a marvelous chess player that I'm surprised he would _____ to sit down at the board with a beginner like me.

8. The "minor difference of opinion" developed into a(n) _____ that split the political party into two opposing factions.

9. The situation is growing worse because there is a(n) _____ of good intentions but a dearth of common sense and willingness to work hard.

10. The stubborn old-timers who refused to sell their homes came to form a(n) _____ of "natives" surrounded by "city people."

11. A good laugh invariably makes me feel better; I honestly believe that it has a(n) _____ effect on my disposition.

12. When the soldiers realized that they had defeated the far more numerous enemy, their cheers rose in a great _____ of jubilation and victory.

13. At the height of Beatlemania in the mid-1960s the Fab Four assumed the stature of pop _____.

14. Although we pride ourselves on the advance of civilization, the sad fact is that the _____ of twentieth-century humanity has resulted in more destruction and suffering than ever before in history.

15. I would have welcomed any firm answer, no matter how unfavorable, but all that I got from her was a(n) _____ smile.

16. When she neatly faked out the guard, pivoted, and drove in for a layup, I realized that I was seeing a true _____ on the basketball court.

17. My classmates selected me to address the community affairs committee because public speaking is a(n) _____ of mine.

18. Once the advance and royalties were settled, the publisher and agent negotiated _____ rights to be covered in the author's contract.

19. The coach used diagrams to show our receivers how to slip through the _____ in our opponent's zone pass coverage.

20. What point is there in dwelling on unproven theories when the problem we are facing demands that we be as _____ as possible?

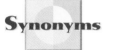

Synonyms

*Choose the word from this unit that is **the same** or **most nearly the same** in meaning as the **boldface** word or expression in the given phrase. Write the word on the line provided.*

1. deign to respond to the question _____

2. wormed its way through the **crevice** _____

3. worshipped the **idol** _____

4. participated in the witty **repartee** _____

5. urges writers to **censor** their screenplays _____

6. offered a **hymn** of praise _____

7. awed by the gifts of the young **master** _____

8. gave their assistance **freely** _____

9. the **curative** benefits of mineral water _____

10. caused a **breech** in their ranks _____

11. received a **surfeit** of gifts _____

12. a charmer, ever ready to **deceive** _____

13. belonging to a **subsidiary** organization _____

14. the **universe** of Western society _____

15. an **island** of safety _____

Antonyms

*Choose the word from this unit that is **most nearly opposite** in meaning to the **boldface** word or expression in the given phrase. Write the word on the line provided.*

16. gave a **crystal-clear** response _____

17. known for their **idealistic** views _____

18. with a **generosity** heretofore unseen _____

19. marked as a **sucker** by the others _____

20. shown not to be a **shortcoming** _____

Choosing the Right Word

*Circle the **boldface** word that more satisfactorily completes each of the following sentences.*

1. The sun left its mottled imprint on the wall as the rays filtered through the (**enclaves, interstices**) of the iron grating.

2. In this situation, when I desperately needed material help, I was deluged with a(n) (**plethora, enclave**) of glib and gratuitous advice.

3. A truly great leader must possess both the inspiration of a visionary and the (**quizzical, pragmatic**) skills of an experienced politician.

4. In the great crises of life, you must depend basically on yourself; the help you get from others can only be (**pragmatic, ancillary**).

5. A political candidate who promises to solve all our social problems without ever mentioning higher taxes would certainly be dismissed as a (**mountebank, schism**).

6. Our little group of would-be writers, painters, and musicians formed an (**enclave, ancillary**) of culture in what we considered a hostile world.

7. Because he sees life as a pattern of ambiguities and contradictions, he likes to express himself in the form of (**quizzical, ancillary**) witticisms.

8. The dictum "There's no such thing as a free lunch" means that nothing worthwhile in life comes to us (**forte, gratis**).

9. They can't force you to do anything, but it is quite possible that they will be able to (**condescend, cozen**) you into actions against your best interests.

10. A theory that seems valid in the confines of a small family group may be proved useless when applied in the (**macrocosm, interstice**) of society at large.

11. Simply because we have dropped a few objectionable words from the dialogue does not justify the critic's statement that we have (**cozened, bowdlerized**) the play.

12. In sandpainting, an art still practiced by the Navajos and Pueblos of the American Southwest, designs are created of (**icons, fortes**) representing animals, deities, and natural phenomena.

13. Your (**virtuosity, pragmatism**) as a public speaker and campaigner may earn you votes, but it cannot make up for your lack of experience and knowledge of public affairs.

14. If, as they say, they find those people so vulgar and unpleasant, why do they (**cozen, condescend**) to associate with them?

15. The clash of wits between those two brilliant columnists was no mere (**persiflage, paean**), but an exchange of deadly insults.

16. The first serious (**schism, enclave**) in the Communist world of the postwar era occurred in 1948, when Yugoslavia began in earnest to distance itself from the Soviet Union.

17. Her easygoing attitude and resilience, far from being a weakness, proved to be her (**mountebank, forte**) in surviving during that trying period.

18. Though acupuncture has been practiced in Eastern medicine for centuries, its (**therapeutic, quizzical**) value has only recently been acknowledged in the West.

19. It is a common mistake to assume that shrewdness in business affairs must be accompanied by extreme (**rapacity, mountebank**).

20. After the great victory, his quiet and modest statements were far more impressive than the most effusive (**paean, interstice**) could have been.

Vocabulary in Context

*Read the following passage, in which some of the words you have studied in this unit appear in **boldface** type. Then complete each statement given below the passage by circling the letter of the item that is **the same** or **almost the same** in meaning as the highlighted word.*

(Line)

Patently Dangerous

In the latter half of the nineteenth century, a **plethora** of diseases plagued Americans living in frontier settlements. Without the benefit of vaccines and antibiotics, an ailing settler was forced to choose from among a variety of grim options. Bleeding and blistering were among the treatments regular, licensed doctors commonly offered.

(5) To treat diphtheria, doctors would boil sulfur in lime water and then pour it into a patient's nose. Dreary procedures like these often compelled the pioneers to seek the aid of unlicensed, less-reputable practitioners, known as irregulars.

Some irregulars extolled the **therapeutic** powers of hot spring waters. Others swore to the efficacy

(10) of the latest patented tonic. Settlers often favored the services of the crafty irregulars, with their patent medicines and promises of good health.

By 1900, the patent-medicine industry offered a vast array of tonics, most full of alcohol and some

(15) containing narcotics or poisons. Lydia Pynkham's Vegetable Compound claimed to cure all kinds of ills; it also contained 18 percent alcohol. Peddlers of the patented tonics managed to **cozen** susceptible patients out of millions of dollars each year. To the

(20) medical community, the patent-medicine industry's increasing **rapacity** and success must have been very disheartening.

Yet within the space of a few years, a group of tireless investigative reporters, nicknamed

(25) muckrakers, kicked off an era of significant reforms. In 1904, Edward Bok published a series of trenchant articles in *Ladies' Home Journal*, exposing the **mountebanks** who ran the patent-medicine industry. In 1906, the American government finally stepped in and passed the Pure Food and Drug Act. It was a small step, but one

(30) that set a precedent for further reforms and cleared the way for the rapid medical advances of the mid-1900s.

This patent medicine promised to cure eight diseases for one dollar!

---

1. The meaning of **plethora** (line 1) is
   a. symbol
   b. shortage
   c. cosmos
   d. glut

2. Therapeutic (line 8) most nearly means
   a. harmful
   b. curative
   c. expert
   d. proven

3. Cozen (line 18) is best defined as
   a. dupe
   b. censor
   c. banter
   d. harm

4. The meaning of **rapacity** (line 21) is
   a. altruism
   b. weakness
   c. aptitude
   d. avarice

5. Mountebanks (line 27) most nearly means
   a. islanders
   b. climbers
   c. swindlers
   d. suckers

REVIEW UNITS 1–3

Visit us at www.sadlier-oxford.com for interactive puzzles and games.

Vocabulary for Comprehension

*Read the following passage, in which some of the words you have studied in Units 1–3 appear in **boldface** type. Then answer questions 1–11 on page 43 on the basis of what is <u>stated</u> or <u>implied</u> in the passage and in the introductory statement.*

This passage focuses on the life of Winslow Homer, one of America's greatest painters.

(Line)

Winslow Homer's dramatic seascapes continue to fascinate museum visitors and collectors. Born in Boston in 1836, he was just
(5) nineteen when his father's importing business soured. Lacking funds for college, he answered an ad and became a lithographer's apprentice. After two years of making bland
(10) drawings, he vowed never to be bound to an employer again.

Homer moved to New York to join the city's artistic community. After a mere five art lessons in night school,
(15) where he learned the basics of oil painting, he boldly embarked on a career as a freelance illustrator. In 1861, under the **aegis** of *Harper's Weekly*, he attached himself to
(20) General George McClellan's Army of the Potomac to draw scenes of Civil War army life in the encampments and at or near the front lines.

His drawings and sketches
(25) showed that he was not a mere realist. His **forte** was his ability to capture the emotional pain and desperation of his subjects, using shape and color to convey his
(30) sympathy for the combatants.

Harper's regularly published his unsentimental images of the fear and despair of Civil War soldiers. By the end of the war, Homer was famous.

(35) Not content to be just another **hideound** artist painting whatever would sell, he traveled to France and, later, to England, where he painted the people of the fishing village of
(40) Tynemouth, whose daily lives were affected by their constant struggles with the sea. Returning to America, in a seemingly puzzling move, he settled in Prout's Neck, finding the
(45) solitude he needed on the remote and rugged Maine coast. His new paintings depicted the drama of man's heroic battles with the forces of nature.

Except for excursions to Florida and
(50) the Caribbean, Homer remained in Maine, far from the celebrity he spurned. Nonetheless, by the late 1880s, he was recognized as America's **virtuoso** seascape painter.
(55) Homer died in 1910. This self-taught, fiercely independent artist fully deserves his exalted place in the **hierarchy** of great American painters.

1. The primary purpose of the passage is to
   a. analyze Winslow Homer's Civil War drawings
   b. highlight the lessons Homer learned on visits to France and England
   c. provide a survey of Homer's life and career
   d. compare and contrast Homer's Civil War drawings and sketches with his seascapes
   e. analyze the reasons for Homer's celebrity

2. From the passage, you can infer that
   a. magazine illustrators were paid very little in Homer's day
   b. more illustrated magazines were published in Boston than in New York
   c. *Harper's Weekly* favored the North over the South in the Civil War
   d. Homer's illustrations in *Harper's Weekly* were a popular success
   e. Homer's Civil War drawings and sketches were highly realistic

3. The meaning of **aegis** (line 18) is
   a. auspices
   b. roof
   c. discipline
   d. employment
   e. scrutiny

4. Which of the following best identifies the writer's focus in paragraph 3 (lines 24–30)?
   a. the importance of realism
   b. Homer's sympathy for his subjects
   c. Homer's use of shape and color
   d. the desperation of the combatants
   e. Homer's emotional pain

5. **Forte** (line 26) most nearly means
   a. fortress
   b. foible
   c. strong suit
   d. weakness
   e. habit

6. From the passage, you can infer that
   a. Homer traveled to France and England because he was dissatisfied with life in the United States

   b. Homer grew disillusioned with daily life in England
   c. Homer found no suitable subjects to paint in England
   d. Homer's fame in England soon equaled his fame in America
   e. Homer's decision to travel to France and England grew from a desire to widen his artistic horizons

7. **Hidebound** (line 36) is best defined as
   a. clothed
   b. narrow-minded
   c. flexible
   d. enfeebled
   e. unknown

8. Which of the following best describes the organizational structure of the passage?
   a. order of importance
   b. spatial order
   c. cause and effect
   d. chronological order
   e. comparison and contrast

9. **Virtuoso** (line 54) most nearly means
   a. virtuous
   b. amateur
   c. masterly
   d. mediocre
   e. leading

10. **Hierarchy** (line 58) is best defined as
    a. court
    b. history
    c. anecdotes
    d. pecking order
    e. family

11. Which of the following best describes the author's attitude toward the subject?
    a. humorous
    b. skeptical
    c. caustic
    d. admiring
    e. neutral

Grammar in Context

In the sentence "Lacking funds for college, he answered an ad and became a lithographer's apprentice" (lines 6–8 on page 42), the modifying phrase "Lacking funds for college" describes "he." However, if the author had placed the modifying phrase at the end of the sentence, it would have illogically modified "lithographer's apprentice." A modifying phrase or clause that is placed too far away from the word it logically modifies is called a **misplaced modifier**.

Because a misplaced modifier is incorrectly placed, it does not describe the word for which it is logically intended. Instead, it modifies another word—sometimes with comical results. To correct a misplaced modifier, move it as close as possible to the word it is meant to modify, or reword the sentence. For example, in the following sentence, the modifier is misplaced: "I finished reading the book that Professor Cary wrote about Winslow Homer <u>during spring break</u>." Here is the same sentence with the modifying phrase in the correct place: "<u>During spring break</u>, I finished reading the book that Professor Cary wrote about Winslow Homer."

On the lines provided, rewrite each sentence in which the modifier is misplaced. Write "correct" if the sentence is correct.

1. The dramatic seascapes continue to fascinate art collectors and museum visitors of Winslow Homer.

_____

_____

2. After two years, he vowed never to be bound again to another employer making bland drawings.

_____

_____

3. Having moved to New York, Homer set out to join the city's artistic community.

_____

_____

4. He learned the basics of oil painting and boldly embarked on a career as a freelance illustrator in night school.

_____

_____

5. Using shape and color, Homer's forte was his ability to capture the emotional pain of Civil War soldiers.

_____

_____

6. Homer finally settled on the remote and rugged Maine coast returning to America.

_____

_____

Word Associations

In each of the following groups, circle the word that is best defined or suggested by the given phrase.

1. "For you, our special customer, it's on the house."
a. gratis　　　b. polarized　　　c. quizzical　　　d. ancillary

2. I'm glad I done it!
a. purview　　　b. verisimilitude　　　c. aegis　　　d. solecism

3. He certainly fooled us!
a. proselyte　　　b. mountebank　　　c. virtuoso　　　d. vassal

4. delighted to listen to their clever give-and-take
a. persiflage　　　b. paean　　　c. lexicon　　　d. paternalism

5. It's hardly worth bothering about.
a. effete　　　b. minuscule　　　c. pragmatic　　　d. sanguine

6. The chairperson brought the committee up to date on the new developments.
a. apprise　　　b. caterwaul　　　c. defer　　　d. bowdlerize

7. Is it inside or outside of our jurisdiction?
a. enclave　　　b. forte　　　c. purview　　　d. claque

8. The instincts of a "shark"
a. rapacity　　　b. plethora　　　c. melee　　　d. raillery

9. like nails on a chalkboard
a. caterwaul　　　b. polarize　　　c. obfuscate　　　d. deracinate

10. looking at the large picture
a. verisimilitude　　　b. icon　　　c. macrocosm　　　d. persiflage

11. a person's "long suit"
a. interstice　　　b. lexicon　　　c. aegis　　　d. forte

12. "It's no use crying over spilled milk."
a. hierarchy　　　b. fait accompli　　　c. schism　　　d. vignette

Choosing the Right Meaning

Read each sentence carefully. Then circle the item that best completes the statement below the sentence.

Adopting the role of virtuoso, newspaper magnate William Randolph Hearst scoured Europe in the 1920s for antiques and objets d'art with which to furnish San Simeon, his immense California estate.　　(2)

1. In line 1 the word **virtuoso** is used to mean
a. maestro　　　b. prodigy　　　c. tycoon　　　d. connoisseur

Despite the claims advanced in commercials, I find it hard to believe that one brand
of paper towel is more bibulous than another. (2)

2. The best definition for the word **bibulous** in line 2 is

a. absorbent   b. inebrious   c. fond of the bottle   d. soft

"This fellow here, with envious carping tongue,
Upbraided me about the rose I wear; (2)
Saying, the sanguine color of the leaves
Did represent my master's blushing cheeks . . ." (4)
        (Shakespeare, *I Henry VI*, IV, i, 90–93)

3. In line 3 the word **sanguine** most nearly means

a. cheerful   b. red   c. optimistic   d. confident

Attached to units of the Red Army were political commissars, Communist party
ideologues whose pragmatic and tyrannical ways made them the objects of fear (2)
and contempt on the part of the common soldiers.

4. The word **pragmatic** in line 2 most nearly means

a. practical   b. businesslike   c. doctrinaire   d. conspiratorial

Antonyms

*In each of the following groups, circle the word or expression that is
most nearly the **opposite** of the word in **boldface** type.*

1. quizzical
a. amused
b. unequivocal
c. contorted
d. dissimilar

2. paean
a. lament
b. sonnet
c. soliloquy
d. appear

3. deracinate
a. implant
b. twist
c. conceal
d. flourish

4. quasi
a. tacitly
b. noisily
c. semi
d. completely

5. chimerical
a. impossible
b. fortunate
c. comprehensive
d. realistic

6. poltroon
a. follower
b. stalwart
c. milksop
d. employer

7. proselyte
a. gallant
b. novice
c. guide
d. proper

8. eleemosynary
a. unworthy
b. uncharitable
c. unenthusiastic
d. unemployable

9. noisome
a. wholesome
b. quiet
c. tasty
d. loathsome

10. oblivious
a. thankful
b. tolerant
c. smug
d. cognizant

11. ancillary
a. dependent
b. concomitant
c. relevant
d. primary

12. plethora
a. surfeit
b. dearth
c. contrast
d. supply

13. effete
a. vigorous
b. exhausted
c. lax
d. awkward

14. pragmatic
a. earthy
b. prominent
c. idealistic
d. inquisitive

15. bibulous
a. limited
b. sedate
c. abstemious
d. convivial

16. obfuscate
a. bedim
b. exemplify
c. clarify
d. slander

Completing the Sentence

From the following list of words, choose the one that best completes each of the following sentences. Write the word in the space provided.

condescend	hierarchy	macrocosm	rapacity
cozen	interstice	quasi	sanguine

1. He quickly learned his lowly place in the _____ of employees in the busy supermarket.

2. How could you have allowed them to _____ you into voting for their ticket?

3. Will Earth be able to survive the _____ of humanity in the name of progress?

4. I was amazed that the august senior would _____ to allow me to drive him home.

5. Even a person of his _____ temperament could not maintain his optimism in the face of such a series of misfortunes.

6. She soon learned to fill the _____ between the intense workouts with relaxation exercises.

Word Families

A. *On the line provided, write the word you have learned in Units 1–3 that is related to each of the following nouns.*
EXAMPLE: obfuscation—**obfuscate**

1. condescension _____

2. deracination _____

3. bowdlerization, bowdlerizer _____

4. polarization, polarity _____

5. pragmatism, pragmatist _____

6. chimera, chimerism _____

7. lachrymosity _____

8. indigenousness _____

9. therapy, therapist, therapeutics _____

10. oblivion, obliviousness _____

11. ribaldry _____

12. liturgist, liturgiology _____

13. poltroonery _____

14. vignettist _____

15. claqueur _____

16. lexicology, lexicographer _____

B. *On the line provided, write the word you have learned in Units 1–3 that is related to each of the following verbs.*
EXAMPLE: indigenize—**indigenous**

17. proselytize   _____

18. quiz   _____

19. schismatize   _____

20. supinate   _____

Two-Word Completions   *Circle the pair of words that best complete the meaning of each of the following passages.*

1. As the detachment of knights galloped over the crest of the hill, it collided with a column of enemy foot soldiers moving up the other side. In the brief but bloody _____ that ensued, two of the king's most prominent _____ lost their lives, and the Duke of Orleans was wounded.
a. schism . . . proselytes
b. purview . . . mountebanks
c. melee . . . vassals
d. vignette . . . bellwethers

2. Your composition is so full of _____, malapropisms, and general gobbledygook that I suggest you study a grammar book, a _____, and a style manual before you ever again put pen to paper.
a. interstices . . . liturgy
b. raillery . . . microcosm
c. persiflage . . . plethora
d. solecisms . . . lexicon

3. The social structure of the South in the days before the Civil War was rigidly _____, with the gentleman planter at the summit of the edifice and the chattel slave at its base. _____ notions of caste discouraged whites from moving freely within the system, and the "peculiar institution" denied blacks any mobility whatsoever.
a. pragmatic . . . Polarized
b. hierarchical . . . Hidebound
c. therapeutic . . . Cozened
d. chimerical . . . Obfuscated

4. On more than one occasion during the Middle Ages, controversy about some point of doctrine _____ ecclesiastical opinion and produced a temporary _____ in the Christian church.
a. polarized . . . schism
b. bowdlerized . . . fait accompli
c. obfuscated . . . enclave
d. deracinated . . . macrocosm

Building with Classical Roots

sem, simil, simul—like; together, at the same time

This root appears in **verisimilitude** (page 30), which means "the appearance of being true." Some other words based on the same root are listed below.

assemblage	**disassemble**	**simile**	**simulation**
assimilation	**resemblance**	**simulacrum**	**simulcast**

From the list of words above, choose the one that corresponds to each of the brief definitions below. Write the word in the blank space in the illustrative sentence below the definition.

1. an image or representation of something; an unreal or superficial semblance

The first 1950s television sitcoms presented a cheery _____ of family happiness.

2. to take apart

After the science fair, it took the exhibitors and maintenance crew several hours to fully _____ the many displays and booths.

3. a similarity in form or appearance; a likeness

Grandma glows over the strong family _____ she already sees in her newborn grandson.

4. a collection of people or things; a gathering

The most experienced journalists were sent to cover the annual _____ of notables in the field of medical research.

5. a comparison, introduced by *like* or *as*; an analogy

A nonfiction essay on a dreary topic can be enlivened by poetic use of _____.

6. the act or process of taking in or absorbing; the state of being absorbed

The healthy human brain is uniquely designed for constant _____ of knowledge.

7. to broadcast over radio and television at the same time

She had some friends over to enjoy the _____ of the rock concert with her.

8. the act or process of taking on the appearance or form of something; a feigning or pretending

Although the children were unable to keep the secret from their mother, she put on a convincing _____ of surprise at the presentation of their gift.

From the list of words above, choose the one that best completes each of the following sentences. Write the word in the space provided.

1. French purists have gone to great lengths to resist any further _____ of English words and phrases into their language.

2. Displayed in Madame Tussaud's museum in London are _____ fashioned in wax of historical personages and notorious criminals.

3. We watched the _____ of Puccini's *La Boheme* on television while listening to it on our local public radio station.

4. The mechanic was forced to _____ the entire transmission in order to replace the faulty part.

5. The instructor cautioned his creative-writing students against relying on such timeworn _____ as "red as a rose" and "blue as the sky."

6. Members of the police emergency negotiating team rehearse their demanding roles in lifelike _____ of hostage situations.

7. It was a matchless _____ of politicians and philosophers who gathered in Philadelphia in 1787 to frame our Constitution.

8. Though they were not related by blood, the _____ between them was so strong that many took them for sisters.

Circle the **boldface** word that more satisfactorily completes each of the following sentences.

1. In American studies class, we prepared a detailed (**simulation, assemblage**) of the landmark *Brown v. Board of Education* case that the U.S. Supreme Court heard in 1954.

2. Part of a soldier's basic training is to learn to (**simulcast, disassemble**) and then put back together a weapon, within a time limit, while blindfolded.

3. In many cases, sociologists have noted that the younger the immigrant, the more likely his or her (**simulation, assimilation**) into the local culture will progress smoothly and quickly.

4. Robert Burns's well-loved poem "A Red, Red Rose" begins with two very basic yet romantic (**resemblances, similes**) about the object of the poet's affection.

5. In the closing credits for most movies, you will see in small print a legal disclaimer that any (**resemblance, simulacrum**) to actual persons, living or dead, is purely coincidental.

6. The pageantry of the opening ceremonies of the Olympic Games is a thrilling experience for the (**assemblage, assimilation**) of world-class athletes who take part.

7. It takes advanced planning, flexible scheduling, and technological precision to effectively (**disassemble, simulcast**) a program on two media.

8. In recurring dreams, he was tormented by the astonishing (**simile, simulacrum**) of the horrific fire he had witnessed as a young child.

Definitions

Note carefully the spelling, pronunciation, part(s) of speech, and definition(s) of each of the following words. Then write the word in the blank space(s) in the illustrative sentence(s) following. Finally, study the lists of synonyms and antonyms given at the end of each entry.

1. affinity
(ə fin′ ə te)

(*n.*) a natural attraction to a person, thing, or activity; a relationship, connection

The mysterious _____ between the two leaders could not be explained.

SYNONYMS: inclination, penchant
ANTONYMS: distaste, aversion

2. bilious
(bil′ yəs)

(*adj.*) peevish or irritable; sickeningly unpleasant

The room was painted a _____ shade of green.

SYNONYMS: choleric, irascible, peevish, splenetic
ANTONYMS: sweet-tempered, genial, pleasant, delightful

3. cognate
(kog′ nāt)

(*adj.*) closely related in origin, essential nature, or function; (*n.*) such a person or thing

_____ languages, such as Spanish, Italian, and French, share a common root.

When I studied Latin, I learned that the words *pater* and *father* are _____.

SYNONYMS: (*adj.*) allied, affiliated; (*n.*) relative
ANTONYMS: (*adj.*) dissimilar, unrelated

4. corollary
(kôr′ ə ler ē)

(*n.*) a proposition that follows from one already proven; a natural consequence or result; (*adj.*) resultant or consequent

Learning the axiom and its _____ was no simple matter.

The _____ effects of today's findings remain to be seen.

SYNONYMS: (*n.*) deduction, conclusion
ANTONYMS: (*n.*) axiom, postulate, premise

5. cul-de-sac
(kəl′ də sak)

(*n.*) a blind alley or dead-end street; any situation in which further progress is impossible; an impasse

Much to their dismay, the once-optimistic negotiators found themselves in a hopeless _____.

6. derring-do
(der′ iŋ dü)

(*n.*) valor or heroism; daring deeds or exploits (often used to poke fun at false heroics)

Breathtaking feats of _____ are all in a day's work for a Hollywood stuntperson.

SYNONYMS: audacity, bravado, pyrotechnics
ANTONYMS: cowardice, timidity, poltroonery

7. divination
(div ə nā′ shən)

(*n.*) the art or act of predicting the future or discovering hidden knowledge

Claiming skill in _____, the fortune teller took my money and then told me what my future held.

SYNONYMS: prophesy, augury

8. elixir
(i lik′ sər)

(*n.*) a potion once thought capable of curing all ills and maintaining life indefinitely; a panacea; a sweet liquid used as a vehicle in medicines

Allegedly, the explorer Ponce de León spent years searching for the _____ of eternal life.

SYNONYMS: cure-all, nostrum, tonic

9. folderol
(fol′ də rol)

(*n.*) foolish talk, ideas, or procedures; nonsense; a trifle

Right from the outset, the sergeant informed her troops that she would not tolerate any _____.

SYNONYMS: hoopla, gibberish
ANTONYMS: sense, significance

10. gamut
(gam′ ət)

(*n.*) an entire range or series

The reviews of the newest Broadway musical extravaganza ran the _____ from praise to scorn.

SYNONYMS: scope, compass, sweep

11. hoi polloi
(hoi pə loi′)

(*n.*) the common people, the masses

By catering to the _____, the studio was able to make one very successful movie after another.

SYNONYM: rank and file
ANTONYMS: aristocracy, elite, upper class

12. ineffable
(in ef′ ə bəl)

(*adj.*) not expressible in words; too great or too sacred to be uttered

The _____ joy of parenthood is the subject of a psychologist's new bestseller.

SYNONYMS: inexpressible, indescribable

13. lucubration
(lü kyủ brā′ shən)

(*n.*) laborious study or thought, especially at night; the result of such work

The scientist's _____ took place after midnight, secretly, in the quiet of the laboratory.

SYNONYMS: burning the midnight oil, deep thought

14. mnemonic
(ni mon′ ik)

(*adj.*) relating to or designed to assist the memory; (*n.*) a device to aid the memory

PPMDAS is a _____ device used to remember the order of mathematical operations.

The _____ HOMES can help people to recall the names of the Great Lakes.

SYNONYMS: (*n.*) reminder, cue

15. obloquy
(ob′ lə kwē)

(*n.*) public abuse indicating strong disapproval or censure; the disgrace resulting from such treatment

The press heaped _____ on the head of the offending official.

SYNONYMS: discredit, opprobrium, ignominy, dishonor
ANTONYMS: praise, acclaim, approbation

16. parameter
(pə ram′ ə tər)

(*n.*) a determining or characteristic element; a factor that shapes the total outcome; a limit, boundary

The committee analyzed the _____ of the nation's military potential.

17. pundit
(pən′ dit)

(*n.*) a learned person; one who gives authoritative opinions

A renowned _____ of the theater, the critic had the power to affect a show's success.

SYNONYMS: expert, authority, savant
ANTONYMS: layman, amateur, dilettante

18. risible
(riz′ ə bəl)

(*adj.*) pertaining to laughter; able or inclined to laugh; laughable

All in the crowd, not just the children, were delighted by the _____ antics of the clowns.

SYNONYMS: droll, ludicrous
ANTONYMS: depressing, poignant, heartrending

19. symptomatic
(simp tə mat′ ik)

(*adj.*) typical or characteristic; being or concerned with a symptom of a disease

According to certain sociologists, vulgarity and indulgence are _____ of a nation's decline.

SYNONYM: indicative

20. volte-face
(volt fäs′)

(*n.*) an about-face; a complete reversal

The prosecution's witness's testimony amounted to a completely unexpected _____.

SYNONYM: turnabout

Completing the Sentence

From the words for this unit, choose the one that best completes each of the following sentences. Write the word in the space provided.

1. The role calls for an actor who can express a(n) _____ of emotions, from speechless rage to utter bliss.

2. After having strongly supported the teaching of foreign languages, they made a complete _____ and advocated that this part of the curriculum be dropped or limited to a small minority.

3. In reading a passage in French, I can often guess the meanings of words I have never seen before because they are recognizable _____ of familiar English words.

4. The _____ tenor of the remarks that they offered to us as "constructive criticism" betrayed just how sorely they envied our success.

5. The suggestion was so _____ that I couldn't help laughing out loud as soon as I heard it.

6. The intensive merchandising and tremendous sale of patent medicines shows that mankind has never really ceased its search for an all-purpose _____.

7. Foreign visitors sometimes dismiss our national political conventions as mere _____ because of all the surface pageantry.

8. All kittens display a natural _____ for mischief, but I have never known one so bent on monkey business as our Mickie.

9. The relief we felt when we realized they were safe was so profound and overwhelming as to be utterly _____.

10. Is our blind faith in computerized analysis any different in its essentials from the belief of so-called primitive peoples in _____?

11. Having been maneuvered into a(n) _____, the retreating troops could do nothing but turn and fight a battle for survival against superior forces.

12. No sooner did the press conference end than the network correspondent turned to a group of political _____ for an instant analysis.

13. Your ponderous _____ seemed to me intended much more to emphasize your own brilliance and importance than to shed any real light on the subject.

14. It is true that capital punishment has not been proved to be a deterrent to murder, but it would be invalid to draw from this the _____ that it has been proved *not* to be a deterrent.

15. In estimating the relative military strength of the two powers, we must concentrate on the _____ by which ability to carry on modern warfare may be judged.

16. The lecturer said that the soaring crime statistics are _____ of a society in which traditional values and standards are breaking down.

17. This short sentence will serve as a(n) _____ to help you remember the names of the first eight Presidents: "*Will A Jolly Man Make A Jolly Visitor?*"

18. I know that they deserve to be condemned, but I can't bring myself to heap
_____ on them when they are in such a state of disgrace.

19. In a truly democratic society, there are no sharp differences in status and privilege
between self-styled aristocrats and the _____.

20. The situation calls for courage, in the sense of a sustained, resolute, and patient
effort—not occasional feats of _____.

Synonyms

*Choose the word from this unit that is **the same** or **most nearly the same** in meaning as the **boldface** word or expression in the given phrase. Write the word on the line provided.*

1. signs **indicative** of smallpox _____

2. the **augury** of the oracle _____

3. among the **related** procedures _____

4. suffered a torrent of **ignominy** _____

5. the **indescribable** beauty of the canyons _____

6. made a surprising **turnabout** _____

7. wondered what all the **hoopla** was about _____

8. not the **cure-all** the mountebank promised _____

9. led the despondent explorers to a **dead end** _____

10. was less than an obvious **deduction** _____

11. spent the late hours in **deep thought** _____

12. an uncalled-for, **splenetic** retort _____

13. the **scope** of the case before the judge _____

14. the **boundaries** of scientific understanding _____

15. a **memory aid** for recalling the rainbow's colors _____

Antonyms

*Choose the word from this unit that is **most nearly opposite** in meaning to the **boldface** word or expression in the given phrase. Write the word on the line provided.*

16. an **aversion** to the smell of cigars _____

17. was not the time for **timidity** _____

18. considered a **dilettante** by many at the museum _____

19. witnessed a **poignant** performance _____

20. a vacation spot favored by the **upper class** _____

Circle the **boldface** word that more satisfactorily completes each of the following sentences.

1. Your irresponsible behavior has finally caught up with you; you are in a (**cul-de-sac, hoi polloi**) from which it will be all but impossible to extricate yourself.

2. Many sociologists believe that the high divorce rate in the United States is (**symptomatic, ineffable**) of basic strains and flaws in our social structure.

3. In *Inferno*, Dante introduces personages from history and mythology to portray the full (**gamut, folderol**) of human folly and wickedness.

4. Those remarkably accurate predictions were based not on (**derring-do, divination**) but on insight into human nature and the objective elements in the situation.

5. Henry had an excellent chance to make an honorable career for himself, but he seemed to have a fatal (**affinity, corollary**) for easy money and shady deals.

6. I knew that if I ran for public office, I would be exposed to severe criticism, but I never expected such a flood of (**obloquy, elixir**).

7. Is your repeated use of the expression (**cul-de-sac, hoi polloi**) supposed to convey the idea that you are not one of the people?

8. Only a supreme actor could express so eloquently the (**risible, ineffable**) quality of the "thoughts that do often lie too deep for tears."

9. We found it more difficult to master the (**mnemonic, parameter**) than it would have been to memorize the material to which it was keyed.

10. The advice which they offered us with such pretentious solemnity turned out to be nothing more than platitudes and (**folderol, elixir**).

11. No student of anthropology can fail to recognize the (**cognate, corollary**) elements in the cultures of societies which seem to be vastly different from one another.

12. You have had many difficulties in life, but you are helping neither yourself nor others by behaving in such a (**bilious, cognate**) and offensive manner.

13. It may seem to be a paradox, but I believe it is true that only a basically serious person can fully appreciate the (**risible, bilious**) factors in life.

14. The devastating stock market crash of 1929 surprised not only laymen, but Wall Street (**corollaries, pundits**) as well.

15. The first thing we must do is establish the (**parameters, lucubrations**) of the problem, so that we can begin to think in terms of a practical solution.

16. The pithy comments of that brilliant and delightful woman were a(n) (**elixir, cul-de-sac**) that we found extraordinarily exhilarating.

17. In an age of genocide, atomic weapons, and threats of ecological disaster, do you really expect a sensible person to be fascinated by such romantic tales of (**parameters, derring-do**)?

18. We expect to see politicians modify their points of view from time to time, but a sudden, unexpected (**cognate, volte-face**) by a candidate is more than we can tolerate.

19. I have listened to them state that the present situation is hopeless, but I am unwilling to accept the (**gamut, corollary**) that the only course open to us is surrender.

20. It is little short of incredible that all their mountainous (**lucubrations, divinations**) have brought forth that tiny mouse of an idea.

Read the following passage, in which some of the words you have studied in this unit appear in **boldface** type. Then complete each statement given below the passage by circling the letter of the item that is **the same** or **almost the same** in meaning as the highlighted word.

Journalism, Anyone?

(Line)

If you have a special curiosity in the world around you, in local, national, or international current events, you might want to pursue a career in journalism. Journalism jobs are to be had online, in television and radio, and, of course, in the old print stand-bys, newspapers and magazines. Through each of these
(5) media, reporters, reviewers, and editors provide the public with fresh information on a **gamut** of topics. Within the pages of almost any daily paper, one can find articles that range from the deep seriousness of the plight of earthquake victims half-way around
(10) the world to the utter **folderol** of who wore what at a society wedding.

If you have an **affinity** for the pleasures of literature, a job as a book reviewer might be just the
(15) thing. You would spend much of your time doing something you love: reading. But book reviewing, like other careers in journalism, presents certain **parameters** within which the
(20) journalists must function. Like all reporters, columnists, and magazine editors, book reviewers often have to attend to strict word limits. They must meet demanding deadlines and be

A television network's busy newsroom hums with activity round-the-clock.

(25) sure their facts are accurate. So, book reviewers need to be able to read quickly, albeit thoughtfully, and write quickly, too; they have little time to indulge in the luxury of **lucubration**.

To the professional journalist, no idea is **ineffable**. In fact, it might be said that the most important requirement asked of all journalists is to believe in the ability of
(30) words to describe, explain, and evaluate experience.

---

1. The meaning of **gamut** (line 6) is
a. penchant   c. scolded
b. range   d. sense

2. The meaning of **folderol** (line 10) is
a. significance   c. peevishness
b. poltroonery   d. nonsense

3. Affinity (line 12) most nearly means
a. aversion   c. inclination
b. elixir   d. ignominy

4. Parameters (line 19) most nearly means
a. limits   c. senses
b. tonics   d. cues

5. Lucubration (line 27) means
a. timidity   c. deep thought
b. significance   d. aversion

6. Ineffable (line 28) is best defined as
a. droll   c. unrelated
b. inexpressible   d. bilious

Definitions

Note carefully the spelling, pronunciation, part(s) of speech, and definition(s) of each of the following words. Then write the word in the blank space(s) in the illustrative sentence(s) following. Finally, study the lists of synonyms and antonyms given at the end of each entry.

1. aficionado
(ə fish yə nä′ dō)

(*n.*) an enthusiastic and usually expert follower or fan

I have been an _____ of football since my youth.

SYNONYMS: devotee, enthusiast

2. browbeat
(braú′ bēt)

(*v.*) to intimidate by a stern or overbearing manner; to bully

The dissatisfied customer had to _____ the store manager into refunding his money.

SYNONYMS: cow, coerce
ANTONYMS: coax, cajole, wheedle, sweet-talk

3. commensurate
(kə men′ sə rit)

(*adj.*) equal in size, extent, duration, or importance; proportionate; measurable by the same standards

All employees got raises _____ with their efforts.

SYNONYMS: comparable, corresponding, coordinate

4. diaphanous
(dī af′ ə nəs)

(*adj.*) very sheer and light; almost completely transparent

We were asked to use a _____ material like gauze to make the costumes.

SYNONYMS: translucent, gossamer
ANTONYMS: opaque, coarse, dense

5. emolument
(i mol′ yə mənt)

(*n.*) profit derived from an office or position or from employment; a fee or salary

Choosing an equitable _____ for the mayor was the latest of the city council's acts.

SYNONYMS: pay, wages, compensation

6. foray
(fôr′ ā)

(*n.*) a quick raid, especially for plunder; a venture into some field of endeavor; (*v.*) to make such a raid

The cavalry's _____ behind enemy lines was a great success.

Counting on the element of surprise, the general ordered the troops to begin to _____ before dawn.

SYNONYMS: (*n.*) sally, sortie
ANTONYMS: (*n.*) retreat, strategic withdrawal

7. genre
(zhän′ rə)

(*n.*) a type, class, or variety, especially a distinctive category of literary composition; a style of painting in which everyday scenes are realistically depicted

The science fiction _____ has produced several classics.

SYNONYMS: species, sort, school

8. homily
(hom′ ə lē)

(*n.*) a sermon stressing moral principles; a tedious moralizing lecture or discourse

The topic of this week's _____ is respect for diversity.

9. immure
(i myür′)

(*v.*) to enclose or confine within walls; to imprison; to seclude or isolate

The terrorist was _____ for life in a narrow cell.

SYNONYMS: incarcerate, mew up
ANTONYMS: release, liberate, emancipate

10. insouciant
(in sü′ sē ənt)

(*adj.*) blithely indifferent or unconcerned; carefree; happy-go-lucky

After months of worrying about the fate of his new project, the man was determined to lead a more _____ life thereafter.

SYNONYMS: nonchalant, blasé, devil-may-care
ANTONYMS: worried, careworn, agitated, distraught

11. matrix
(mā′ triks)

(*n.*) a mold; the surrounding situation or environment

Scientists discovered a tiny prehistoric creature fossilized in a _____ of amber.

SYNONYMS: pattern, model

12. obsequies
(ob′ sə kwēz)

(*n.*) funeral rites or ceremonies

The nation held somber _____ for their beloved leader.

SYNONYMS: last rites, funeral services

13. panache
(pə nash′)

(*n.*) a confident and stylish manner, dash; a strikingly elaborate or colorful display

In the film *The Adventures of Robin Hood,* the actor Errol Flynn captures the _____ of the bandit.

SYNONYMS: style, verve, élan, éclat, flamboyance

14. persona
(pər sō′ nə)

(*n.*) a character in a novel or play; the outward character or role that a person assumes

The comic _____ of Charlie Chaplin is recognizable the world over.

SYNONYMS: personality, image, role

15. philippic
(fi lip′ ik)

(*n.*) a bitter verbal attack

The senator delivered a _____ against the proposed law and those who supported it.

SYNONYMS: harangue, tirade, diatribe
ANTONYMS: encomium, panegyric, tribute

16. prurient
(prủr′ ē ənt)

(*adj.*) having lustful desires or interests; tending to arouse sexual desires

Considered a _____ novel by some, *Ulysses* was once banned from sale in the United States.

SYNONYMS: lascivious, salacious, lewd, titillating
ANTONYMS: prudish, demure, innocent

17. sacrosanct
(sak′ rō saŋkt)

(*adj.*) very sacred or holy; inviolable; set apart or immune from questioning or attack

Members of the clergy felt privileged to be entrusted with guarding the _____ relic.

18. systemic
(sis tem′ ik)

(*adj.*) of or pertaining to the entire body; relating to a system or systems

The singer suffered a _____ breakdown after the long and demanding season.

SYNONYMS: extensive, comprehensive, system-wide
ANTONYMS: localized, specific, isolated, confined

19. tendentious
(ten den′ shəs)

(*adj.*) intended to promote a particular point of view, doctrine, or cause; biased or partisan

The candidate's supporters heartily applauded her _____ arguments.

SYNONYM: partial
ANTONYMS: fair, impartial, equitable, disinterested

20. vicissitude
(vi sis′ ə tüd)

(*n.*) a change, variation, or alteration; (*pl.*) successive or changing phases or conditions

The inevitable _____ of life affect us all.

SYNONYMS: fluctuation, vacillation
ANTONYMS: sameness, evenness

Completing the Sentence

From the words for this unit, choose the one that best completes each of the following sentences. Write the word in the space provided.

1. Having been conditioned to take wealth and luxury for granted, they tended to take a(n) _____ attitude toward money, even when they had only a modest income.

2. In her speech to the entering freshman class, the dean emphasized that the benefits they derived from any course would be _____ with the effort that they devoted to it.

3. Time after time, he rose on the floor of the Senate and delivered bitter _____ against the lack of effective measures against environmental pollution.

4. In my opinion, the epic poem represents the most noble and inspiring of all literary _____.

5. Their reverence for all creations of God was so great that, in their eyes, even the most common manifestation of nature was _____.

6. One of my fondest hopes is to visit Jerusalem, the city that has had a unique role in history as the _____ of three great world religions.

7. It was a cat-and-mouse play about a patient detective and an aristocratic jewel thief who stole with elegance and _____.

8. The overbearing maitre d' _____ the diners into meekly accepting the least desirable table in the restaurant.

9. When doctors discovered the disease to be _____, they held out little hope for the patient's recovery.

10. When we reflected on his long and happy life and his unmatched record of public service, we found the _____ comforting and even inspiring.

11. She claimed to be an unbiased witness, but I found her testimony to be opinionated and _____.

12. The constitution provides that the _____ received by the President is to be neither increased nor decreased during his term of office.

13. You should not approach a class in sex education with such a leering and _____ attitude.

14. The true test of her character will be how she is able to deal with the _____ of life.

15. She cannot relate to other people in a constructive way because she is _____ in her own prejudices and hostilities.

16. At first she showed only a mild interest in bridge, but as she played more and developed skill, she became a real _____ of the game.

17. Our troops returned from their successful _____ against the enemy's base in a jubilant mood.

18. The omniscient narrator is probably the most common _____ assumed by novel writers.

19. We found overwhelming beauty in the most common manifestations of nature, such as the colors of sunset, the delicate shape of a flower, or the _____ wings of an insect.

20. What good does it do to regale the prisoners with _____ about going straight if they have no chance to make an honest living when they are released?

Synonyms

*Choose the word from this unit that is **the same** or **most nearly the same** in meaning as the **boldface** word or expression in the given phrase. Write the word on the line provided.*

1. a **sermon** on the value of honesty _____

2. **compensation** for the job _____

3. the only true **enthusiast** in the room _____

4. envied their **nonchalant** approach _____

5. the **fluctuations** of the family's daily routines _____

6. was seen as **salacious** behavior _____

7. **incarcerated** in a dungeon _____

8. let loose a searing **tirade** _____

9. possessed a certain **flamboyance** _____

10. in the **role** of a gangster _____

11. considered to be a **sacred** right _____

12. pay **proportionate** to the task _____

13. a good example of that **school** of painting _____

14. used a **model** to solve the logic problem _____

15. delivered the **last rites** _____

Antonyms

*Choose the word from this unit that is **most nearly opposite** in meaning to the **boldface** word or expression in the given phrase. Write the word on the line provided.*

16. made of **coarse** material _____

17. stunned by their **impartial** response _____

18. **coaxed** the players into using the new system _____

19. a **strategic withdrawal** under fire _____

20. reports of **localized** uprisings _____

Choosing the Right Word

*Circle the **boldface** word that more satisfactorily completes each of the following sentences.*

1. I admit that you have some grounds for complaint, but those shrieks of outrage are simply not (**diaphanous, commensurate**) with having been overcharged five cents.

2. It seems incredible that a few generations ago a novel of such quality could be widely condemned as designed to appeal to (**tendentious, prurient**) interests.

3. The fact that they referred to my salary as a(n) (**panache, emolument**) did not disguise the fact that I was being woefully underpaid.

4. How can young people hope to become mature, self-reliant adults if they (**immure, foray**) themselves in a home environment that is so comfortable and protective?

5. It is often said that in Russia there are as many (**vicissitudes, aficionados**) of chess as there are of baseball or golf in the United States.

6. If the woman thinks her status as a public official renders her (**insouciant, sacrosanct**), she is in for a rude awakening.

7. The Bible reminds us that even in moments of great joy we should retain some awareness of the (**panache, vicissitudes**) and heartbreaks of life.

8. What we owe to our fallen leader is not mournful (**philippics, obsequies**) but a joyful assertion of life and a pledge to continue her work.

9. The (**matrix, persona**) that a public figure displays to the world is often quite different from the personality that he or she exhibits in private.

10. Certainly your judgment, if not your motives, must be questioned when you choose to associate yourself with an organization of that (**matrix, genre**).

11. Corot painted poetic and (**diaphanous, tendentious**) landscapes, in which even solid objects seemed to be suffused with light and movement.

12. The defense attorney claimed that the police had used scare tactics to (**browbeat, foray**) her client into a confession.

13. What gourmet feast can compare with the luscious delicacies that we consumed during our midnight (**forays, homilies**) on the well-stocked refrigerator?

14. When the results of the scholarship competition were announced, we could sense the deep disappointment beneath your (**insouciant, tendentious**) manner.

15. The commission found that police corruption was not confined to one or two isolated precincts but was (**systemic, prurient**) in nature.

16. The purpose of our policies is to develop bold new forms of international understanding and practical cooperation that can serve as the (**philippic, matrix**) for a stable peace.

17. There is no doubt of your oratorical talents, but this is a time for quiet words of reconciliation—not for thundering (**emoluments, philippics**).

18. I had hoped to hear a balanced, dispassionate discussion of this problem, but I found their approach to be distressingly one-sided and (**tendentious, sacrosanct**).

19. Young people involved in drug abuse need practical help in overcoming their addiction—not (**homilies, obsequies**) exhorting them to higher standards of behavior.

20. James Bond seems to dispose of the villains he faces with all the (**genre, panache**) of the legendary paladins of medieval romance.

*Read the following passage, in which some of the words you have studied in this unit appear in **boldface** type. Then complete each statement given below the passage by circling the letter of the item that is **the same** or **almost the same** in meaning as the highlighted word.*

Rowdy Ball

(Line)

In the last decade of the nineteenth century, **systemic** dirty play characterized American major league baseball. Players routinely spiked, tripped, and insulted opponents. But the turn of the century brought an end to what was called "rowdy ball." In the twentieth century, baseball was played more cleanly and with more strategy than ever before. (5)

The rules of professional baseball, like those of other sports, are not **sacrosanct**. Some key changes in the 1900s greatly affected the way the game

was played. For the first time, foul balls were recorded as strikes. Accordingly, batting averages (10) dropped and strikeouts rose. Fielders' gloves grew in size. There followed a **commensurate** drop in errors and in runs scored. The balance of power shifted to the (15) pitchers.

In the early 1900s, team rosters were diverse. Many players were the sons of immigrants. Some were college graduates; others were (20)

A batter heads for first base in this 1887 lithograph.

illiterate. Some went back to the mines or the farms in the off-season. Players had nicknames like "Wagon Tongue" and "The Flying Dutchman."

Many different **personas** shared the teams' dugouts. Although teamwork was key, not everybody on a team got along. For example, Joe Tinker and Johnny Evers, who, with Frank Chance, were the first famous double-play combination, did not get along. (25) Off the diamond, the Chicago Cubs players were enemies, but that did not affect their coordination on the field—the two worked together like a well-oiled machine.

The new rules and exciting and entertaining players drew **aficionados** of the game to the new concrete and steel stadiums. Attendance boomed. The modern age of baseball had begun. (30)

---

1. The meaning of **systemic** (line 1) is
a. localized   c. extensive
b. sacred   d. uncommon

2. Sacrosanct (line 7) most nearly means
a. specific   c. reasonable
b. inviolable   d. nonchalant

3. Commensurate (line 13) is best defined as
a. corresponding   c. common
b. salacious   d. partisan

4. The meaning of **personas** (line 23) is
a. sermons   c. devotees
b. styles   d. personalities

5. Aficionados (line 28) most nearly means
a. officials   c. members
b. enthusiasts   d. schools

Definitions

Note carefully the spelling, pronunciation, part(s) of speech, and definition(s) of each of the following words. Then write the word in the blank space(s) in the illustrative sentence(s) following. Finally, study the lists of synonyms and antonyms given at the end of each entry.

1. abortive
(ə bôr′ tiv)

(*adj.*) failing to accomplish an intended aim or purpose; only partially or imperfectly developed

An _____ attempt to seize the throne ended badly for the participants.

SYNONYMS: miscarried, fruitless, premature
ANTONYMS: successful, realized, consummated

2. bruit
(brüt)

(*v.*) to spread news, reports, or unsubstantiated rumors

News of the company's closing and the impending job losses was immediately _____ about the office.

SYNONYMS: noise abroad, broadcast, blazon
ANTONYMS: cover up, conceal, hush up

3. contumelious
(kon tü mē′ lē əs)

(*adj.*) insolent or rude in speech or behavior; insultingly abusive; humiliating

The ambassador's _____ reply was completely unexpected.

SYNONYMS: vituperative, scurrilous, excoriating
ANTONYMS: laudatory, commendatory, deferential

4. dictum
(dik′ təm)

(*n.*) a short saying; an authoritative statement

According to the _____ of the critics, the play is not worth the price of admission.

SYNONYMS: maxim, precept, aphorism, axiom

5. ensconce
(en skons′)

(*v.*) to settle comfortably and firmly in position; to put or hide in a safe place

After a very long, difficult day at work, I gratefully _____ myself in my snug, warm bed.

SYNONYMS: nestle, lodge, entrench
ANTONYMS: unseat, displace, oust

6. iconoclastic
(ī kon ə klas′ tik)

(*adj.*) attacking or seeking to overthrow popular or traditional beliefs, ideas, or institutions

The writer's _____ opinions always seem to stir controversy.

SYNONYMS: image-breaking, irreverent, heretical
ANTONYMS: orthodox, conservative, reverent

7. in medias res
(in med' ē əs
rās')

(*adv.*) in or into the middle of a plot; into the middle of things

Since this episode begins _____,
we need to tape it and watch the earlier installments first.

8. internecine
(int ər nes' ēn)

(*adj.*) mutually destructive; characterized by great slaughter and bloodshed

An _____ feud has existed between
the clans for generations.

SYNONYMS: murderous, savage, ruinous
ANTONYMS: peaceful, harmonious, constructive

9. maladroit
(mal ə droit')

(*adj.*) lacking skill or dexterity; lacking tact, perception, or judgment

The supervisor's _____ interference
revealed a lack of experience.

SYNONYMS: inept, awkward, clumsy, gauche
ANTONYMS: skillful, dexterous, deft, tactful

10. maudlin
(môd' lin)

(*adj.*) excessively or effusively sentimental

The tenor sang a _____ ballad and
then a humorous ditty.

SYNONYMS: mushy, mawkish

11. modulate
(mod' yə lāt)

(*v.*) to change or vary the intensity or pitch; to temper or soften; to regulate, adjust

Asked to _____ their voices, the
choir responded adroitly.

SYNONYMS: adapt, moderate

12. portentous
(pôr ten' təs)

(*adj.*) foreshadowing an event to come; causing wonder or awe; self-consciously weighty, pompous

No one realized just how _____ the
strange events of last week would turn out to be.

SYNONYMS: foreboding, ominous, pretentious
ANTONYMS: auspicious, propitious, encouraging

13. prescience
(presh' əns)

(*n.*) knowledge of events or actions before they happen; foresight

The detectives were skeptical about the psychic's
_____ of the suspect's next crime.

SYNONYM: foreknowledge
ANTONYM: hindsight

14. quid pro quo
(kwid′ prō kwō′)

(*n.*) something given in exchange or return for something else

Before agreeing to give their support, the representatives insisted on some _____.

SYNONYMS: swap, trade

15. salubrious
(sə lü′ brē əs)

(*adj.*) conducive to health or well-being; wholesome

Seeking the _____ effects of sea air, the family headed for a shore vacation.

SYNONYMS: beneficial, healthy, invigorating
ANTONYMS: harmful, unhealthy, deleterious, noxious

16. saturnalian
(sat ər nā′ lyan)

(*adj.*) characterized by riotous or unrestrained revelry or licentiousness

The boisterously _____ spectacle was truly something to behold, even from a distance.

SYNONYMS: dissipated, debauched, orgiastic
ANTONYMS: sedate, prim, decorous, seemly

17. touchstone
(təch′ stōn)

(*n.*) a means of testing worth or genuineness

A work's popularity among succeeding generations is thought to be a _____ of its merit.

SYNONYMS: criterion, yardstick, benchmark

18. traumatic
(traủ mat′ ik)

(*adj.*) so shocking to the emotions as to cause lasting and substantial psychological damage

People may feel the effects of a _____ experience for years afterward.

SYNONYM: jolting
ANTONYMS: soothing, comforting, agreeable, pleasant

19. vitiate
(vish′ ē āt)

(*v.*) to weaken, debase, or corrupt; to impair the quality or value of

_____ by its lack of managerial skill, the company's fortunes went straight downhill.

SYNONYMS: degrade, undermine
ANTONYMS: purify, fortify, strengthen, enhance

20. waggish
(wag′ ish)

(*adj.*) fond of making jokes; characteristic of a joker; playfully humorous or droll

The innkeeper's _____ stories lifted the flagging spirits of the weary travelers.

SYNONYMS: whimsical, jocular
ANTONYMS: serious, grave, grim, dour, humorless

Completing the Sentence

From the words for this unit, choose the one that best completes each of the following sentences. Write the word in the space provided.

1. How can you expect them to cooperate with us unless they receive some reasonable _____ for their efforts?

2. For years, Churchill's warnings about Hitler were dismissed as alarmism; only after the outbreak of World War II did people appreciate his _____.

3. I certainly have no intention of turning my back on them simply because it has been _____ about town they are involved in some sort of scandal.

4. If he would only devote more time in school to serious study and less to _____ pranks, his grades would probably improve.

5. All the evidence presented at such length by their lawyers does not seriously _____ the case against the accused.

6. The deathbed scene might have been effective if it had been played with restraint, but their woefully ham-handed acting turned it into a(n) _____ tearjerker.

7. What we are facing in this organization is not healthy competition among the executives but a(n) _____ struggle that will destroy the company.

8. To gain the immediate attention of the reader, the short-story writer sometimes begins a narrative _____, rather than at the very beginning of events.

9. More than anything else, the ability to create distinctive characters and make them come alive on the page is the _____ of a great novelist.

10. Though the critic still has nothing good to say about modern art, age and experience have somewhat _____ the intensity of his disapproval.

11. I was an extremely sensitive child, and the death of my beloved mother certainly had a(n) _____ effect upon me.

12. If you are so _____ in handling your own personal affairs, how you can presume to advise others how to manage their lives?

13. It is one thing to offer a personal opinion; it is quite another to issue a(n) _____ as through you were the only one with any knowledge of the subject.

14. And such are the quirks of fate that there she was, after all her mishaps and blunders, firmly _____ as the president of the firm.

15. In our bored and depressed mood, her buoyant personality had a most _____ effect.

16. The coach devised a clever strategy, but it proved _____ when our team failed to execute it properly.

17. Though the guests at the gala benefit tried to maintain an air of cheer, the _____ news of the international crisis hung like a pall over the gathering.

18. A group of elderly people sitting about sipping tea and discussing the weather is scarcely my idea of _____ revelry.

19. The speaker paid no attention to the _____ remarks of a few hecklers in the crowd but went right on with her speech.

20. Since she thoroughly enjoys taking potshots at sacred cows, I'd describe her attitude as definitely _____ .

Synonyms

*Choose the word from this unit that is **the same** or **most nearly the same** in meaning as the **boldface** word or expression in the given phrase. Write the word on the line provided.*

1. a **beneficial** aspect of the trip _____

2. would **undermine** all our achievements _____

3. heard the familiar **maxim** _____

4. **clumsy** efforts at reconciliation _____

5. a **yardstick** by which a play's success is gauged _____

6. undone by a lack of **foresight** _____

7. one debater's **scurrilous** remarks _____

8. **moderated** my tone of voice _____

9. **nestled** in a favorite chair _____

10. thwarted by **savage** antagonisms _____

11. made a **premature** attempt _____

12. quickly **broadcast** the results _____

13. moved by the **sentimental** story _____

14. agreed upon a reasonable **swap** _____

15. joined the story **in the middle** _____

Antonyms

*Choose the word from this unit that is **most nearly opposite** in meaning to the **boldface** word or expression in the given phrase. Write the word on the line provided.*

16. their usual **sedate** behavior _____

17. the event's **propitious** beginning _____

18. holds **orthodox** views on the subject _____

19. a thoroughly **agreeable** experience _____

20. a **dour** group waiting at the ticket window _____

Choosing the Right Word

Circle the **boldface** word that more satisfactorily completes each of the following sentences.

1. With her elegance and remarkable feel for style, is it any wonder that she soon became (**modulated, ensconced**) as the arbiter of fashion?

2. Prior to the Wright brothers' first successful airplane flight in 1903, all of mankind's efforts to fly had been (**internecine, abortive**).

3. Some people seem to be natural nonconformists; for them (**prescience, iconoclasm**) is not just a mood or an affectation but a way of life.

4. Willy-nilly, parents often enter (**in medias res, waggishly**) into a quarrel between siblings, especially when lasting damage seems about to occur.

5. Historians believe that the Civil War had a collective (**traumatic, salubrious**) impact, which was not healed until a new generation had grown to maturity.

6. My plan to run in the primaries will not be diverted by the (**touchstone, dicta**) of so-called experts who assert that I have no chance of winning.

7. I felt that I had stated my case with sincerity and conviction, but my heart sank when they reacted with a (**maladroit, portentous**) silence.

8. Even the most hardened campaigner might be expected to cringe when subjected to that kind of (**maudlin, contumelious**) treatment.

9. The decline in the value of the company's stock was attributed to the fact that rumors of a contract cancellation had been widely (**bruited, vitiated**).

10. Their efforts to settle the differences between the two factions were so (**portentous, maladroit**) that what had begun as a rift became a chasm.

11. In spite of my extreme nervousness, I made every effort to (**modulate, bruit**) my voice and speak the first lines in a calm, controlled manner.

12. A rugged sense of honesty, marked by a refusal to take refuge in clever ambiguities, has been the (**touchstone, dictum**) of my career in politics.

13. Our hope for peace rests basically on the belief that the great powers now realize that warfare has become too (**internecine, saturnalian**) to risk.

14. Their cool and detached skepticism, which I would have resented under other circumstances, now struck me as a(n) (**iconoclastic, salubrious**) factor in that highly emotionalized situation.

15. When the miners arrived with all of their back pay and intent upon "having fun," our town soon took on the aspect of a frontier (**saturnalia, quid pro quo**).

16. Although those supposedly (**abortive, waggish**) remarks were dressed in the guise of humor, they betrayed a strong undertone of resentment.

17. The concessions which we are making are manifest, but I do not perceive a reasonable (**prescience, quid pro quo**) from the other side.

18. All the snide rumors that have been spread about them do not (**vitiate, ensconce**) their solid reputation for authentic kindness and decency.

19. They survived the critical years due to their uncanny (**prescience, touchstone**) which enabled them to anticipate the moves of their enemies.

20. In that situation, I don't know which was more distressing—the callous indifference of some of my "friends" or the (**maudlin, contelumious**) sympathy of others.

Vocabulary in Context

Read the following passage, in which some of the words you have studied in this unit appear in **boldface** type. Then complete each statement given below the passage by circling the letter of the item that is **the same** or **almost the same** in meaning as the highlighted word.

Someone Who Made a Difference

(Line)

Daisy Bates was born in a small Arkansas mill town in 1920. **Traumatic** experiences in her childhood could have led to a lifetime of anger. Her father, however, encouraged her to focus her energies on fighting discrimination. Bates later said this "priceless heritage" sustained her throughout her life.

(5) In 1941, Bates married L. C. Bates. Together, they published the *Arkansas State Press*, an **iconoclastic** and influential African American newspaper, which championed civil rights and attacked the abuses of segregation. The Bateses moved to Little Rock, where Bates joined the NAACP and became (10) its state president. It was in Little Rock that Daisy Bates joined a local battle that made her famous.

Schools in the segregated South **vitiated** the education of black children. (15) Bates herself had attended inferior schools and had used outdated books. In 1954, when the United States Supreme Court declared segregation in public schools unconstitutional, Bates led the (20) fight to integrate the Little Rock School District. Despite threats to her safety and property, she acted as advocate for and

Daisy Bates, Thurgood Marshall, and Little Rock students at the Supreme Court, 1958

mentor to the nine students who were selected to desegregate Central High School. On September 25, 1957, federal troops sent by President Eisenhower escorted the (25) nine students past jeering mobs and into the building. This struggle was the **touchstone** of Bates' commitment to justice and equality.

Daisy Bates devoted her life to helping African Americans achieve better lives and continually spoke out against injustice. She received more than 200 medals, citations, and other awards, and was honored by four American presidents. (30) Daisy Bates died in Little Rock on November 4, 1999.

---

1. The meaning of **traumatic** (line 1) is
a. memorable   c. jolting
b. strengthened   d. regulated

2. The meaning of **iconoclastic** (line 6) is
a. heretical   c. fruitless
b. orthodox   d. reverent

3. Vitiated (line 14) most nearly means
a. upgraded   c. impaired
b. whimsical   d. sentimental

4. Touchstone (line 26) most nearly means
a. maxim   c. jewel
b. benchmark   d. ruination

REVIEW UNITS 4–6

Visit us at www.sadlier-oxford.com
for interactive puzzles and games.

Vocabulary for Comprehension

*Read the following passage, in which some of the words you have studied in Units 4–6 appear in **boldface** type. Then answer questions 1–10 on page 73 on the basis of what is <u>stated</u> or <u>implied</u> in the passage and in the introductory statement.*

Pinning down historical facts can be tricky, as this passage about the invention of eyeglasses demonstrates.

(Line)

By the end of the thirteenth century, people began to see the world in a new light, for it was about that time that eyeglasses were invented. But

(5) **forays** into the question of precisely when they were invented and by whom have been inconclusive, **tendentious**, and filled with intrigue.

Researchers have put forth

(10) candidates from several European countries and China. Although the exact identity of the inventor has not as yet been established conclusively, he or she was most likely an Italian

(15) glassblower working in the 1280s. The evidence favors either Alessandro Spina or Salvino Armato, with a slight edge to Armato. Armato was an optical physicist who is believed

(20) to have contrived correcting lenses to improve his own vision.

In 1289, the Italian writer Sandro di Popozo refers to eyeglasses as having "recently been invented." Popozo

(25) writes about the advantages afforded by the lenses but never mentions the inventor's name. A second reference appears seventeen years later in a sermon by the friar Giordano di Rivalto.

(30) In the sermon, the friar refers to the nearly 20-year-old art of making

eyeglasses. He, too, neglects to provide us with the name of the inventor.

(35) No matter who invented them, spectacles caught on quickly. But they were not for everybody. The high cost kept them from the **hoi polloi**, and the fact that all lenses were

(40) convex made these "eye disks" "**elixirs**" for the farsighted only. (Concave lenses, which help the nearsighted, first appeared more than a century later.) In addition, the lenses

(45) were hard to wear. The now-familiar stiff frames that loop over our ears were not developed for another 400 years.

Despite the limitations of these early eyeglasses, sales were brisk, and

(50) Italian craftspeople churned them out. The rest is history.

1. The meaning of **forays** (line 5) is
   a. retreats
   b. ventures
   c. attacks
   d. looks
   e. relays

2. Tendentious (line 8) most nearly means
   a. cantankerous
   b. partisan
   c. impartial
   d. tentative
   e. libelous

3. The primary purpose of the passage is
   a. to explain
   b. to reflect
   c. to refute
   d. to persuade
   e. to entertain

4. From paragraph 2 (lines 9–21), it is clear that eyeglasses were probably invented
   a. in China
   b. by the Italian writer Sandro di Popozo
   c. by a friar named Giordano di Rivalto
   d. by an Italian glassblower in the 1280s
   e. by Alessandro Spina

5. The evidence cited in paragraph 3 (lines 22–34) serves primarily to
   a. confirm that Salvino Armato invented eyeglasses
   b. refute the reliability of Sandro di Popozo and Giordano di Rivalto
   c. establish the writer's credentials as an expert on the subject
   d. reveal the writer's skepticism as a historian
   e. strengthen the theory that eyeglasses were invented during the 1280s

6. Which of the following best describes the organizational structure of paragraph 4 (lines 35–47)?
   a. comparison and contrast
   b. chronological order
   c. order of importance
   d. order of impression
   e. cause and effect

7. Hoi polloi (line 38) is best defined as
   a. elite
   b. royalty
   c. masses
   d. merchants
   e. clergy

8. The meaning of **elixirs** (line 41) is
   a. cure-alls
   b. accessories
   c. prophesies
   d. lenses
   e. tools

9. According to the author, concave lenses first appeared
   a. in the 1500s
   b. in the 1600s
   c. about twenty years after the invention of convex lenses
   d. more than a century after the invention of convex lenses
   e. when prices for convex lenses started to decrease

10. Which of the following would be the most appropriate vehicle for publication of this passage?
   a. an article in a technical journal
   b. an entry in a travel guide to Italy
   c. a brief magazine article
   d. a letter to the editor of a daily newspaper
   e. an advertisement for an optician's shop

Grammar in Context

In the sentence "But forays into the question of precisely when they were invented and by whom have been inconclusive, tendentious, and filled with intrigue" (lines 4–8 on page 72), the **plural verb** "have been" agrees with the **plural subject** "forays." Correct writing requires proper **subject-verb agreement**. Note that the number of the subject (singular or plural) is not affected by a phrase or clause that intervenes between the subject and the verb. Singular subjects joined by *or* or *nor* take a singular verb. When a singular subject and a plural subject are joined by *or* or *nor*, the verb agrees with the subject nearer the verb. Collective noun subjects such as *class* and *jury* take singular verbs when the noun refers to the group as a unit; they take plural verbs when the noun refers to the parts or members of the group. A verb should always agree with its subject, not its predicate nominative. Subjects preceded by *every* or *many a* take singular verbs.

Special problems in agreement arise when the subject is an indefinite pronoun. The following indefinite pronouns are always singular: *anyone*, *each*, *either*, *everyone*, *neither*, *no one*, *nothing*, *one*, and *someone*. These indefinite pronouns are always plural: *both*, *few*, *many*, and *several*. The following indefinite pronouns may be singular or plural: *all*, *any*, *most*, *none*, and *some*. A noun in a prepositional phrase often offers a clue to the number of an indefinite pronoun.

Choose the verb in parentheses that agrees with the subject of the sentence, and write it on the line provided.

1. Many a researcher (**has/have**) inquired into the origin of eyeglasses.

_____

2. However, the exact identity of the inventor of spectacles (**has/have**) not been determined.

_____

3. Either Alessandro Spina or Salvino Armato (**seems/seem**) favored by the evidence.

_____

4. The writings of Sandro di Popozo (**mentions/mention**) the advantages of eyeglasses.

_____

5. A pair of spectacles (**is/are**) a necessity for some readers.

_____

6. In the thirteenth century, all the lenses manufactured in Italy (**was/were**) convex in shape.

_____

7. A team of experts (**is/are**) united in the opinion that eyeglasses in those days were for the farsighted only.

_____

8. Despite the limitations of early eyeglasses, brisk sales (**was/were**) an attainable goal for good craftspeople.

_____

Word Associations

In each of the following groups, circle the word that is best defined or suggested by the given phrase.

1. where the *Aeneid* starts
   a. in medias res   b. sacrosanct   c. ensconce   d. pundit

2. Get as good as you give.
   a. dictum   b. gamut   c. quid pro quo   d. affinity

3. cold springwater after a six-mile summertime jog
   a. touchstone   b. matrix   c. dictum   d. elixir

4. Let me look into the crystal ball for you.
   a. persona   b. divination   c. obsequies   d. genre

5. how a bird in a gilded cage might feel
   a. risible   b. immured   c. symptomatic   d. ineffable

6. a sudden about-face
   a. volte-face   b. affinity   c. emolument   d. dictum

7. the ups and downs of life
   a. genres   b. obsequies   c. vicissitudes   d. philippics

8. How did you know that this would happen?
   a. panache   b. prescience   c. cognate   d. gamut

9. the endless bickering that is tearing apart a family
   a. internecine   b. risible   c. salubrious   d. contumelious

10. see-through curtains
   a. ineffable   b. diaphanous   c. tendentious   d. portentous

11. You have to have style!
   a. prescience   b. persona   c. dictum   d. panache

12. Spring, forward; fall, back.
   a. parameter   b. cul-de-sac   c. folderol   d. mnemonic

Choosing the Right Meaning

Read each sentence carefully. Then circle the item that best completes the statement below the sentence.

> "The Moor replies
> That he you hurt is of great fame in Cyprus,   (2)
> and great affinity, and that in wholesome wisdom
> He might not but refuse you." (Shakespeare, *Othello*, III, i, 43–46)   (4)

1. The phrase [**of**] **great affinity** in line 3 is used to mean

   a. widely connected   c. much attracted
   b. naturally inclined   d. very powerful

In some religions the name of the deity is considered ineffable, and believers forbear
to utter it for fear of inviting divine retribution. (2)

2. In line 1 the word **ineffable** is used to mean

a. utterly inexpressible   c. absolutely indescribable

b. too sacred to be spoken   d. unknowable

They who ensconced the papyrus and leather documents now known as the Dead
Sea Scrolls could scarcely have dreamed that nearly two thousand years would (2)
pass before the manuscripts they had hidden would see light of day once more.

3. In line 1 the word **ensconced** most nearly means

a. nestled   b. settled   c. entrenched   d. hid

Since the common cold is caused by a viral infection for which there is as yet no
cure, medicine can do no more than offer a symptomatic treatment of the malady. (2)

4. The word **symptomatic** in line 2 most nearly means

a. characteristic   c. typically old-fashioned

b. indicative   d. relating to symptoms

Antonyms

*In each of the following groups, circle the word or expression that
is most nearly the **opposite** of the word in **boldface** type.*

1. vitiate
a. enhance
b. destroy
c. create
d. debase

2. risible
a. falling
b. slanderous
c. heartrending
d. indirect

3. cognate
a. unrelated
b. expensive
c. recent
d. weird

4. insouciant
a. open
b. distraught
c. conditional
d. guarded

5. tendentious
a. peaceful
b. disinterested
c. argumentative
d. violent

6. contumelious
a. provocative
b. complimentary
c. disdainful
d. ample

7. folderol
a. trifle
b. humor
c. sense
d. sentiment

8. portentous
a. silly
b. dispassionate
c. auspicious
d. immature

9. salubrious
a. tasty
b. hygienic
c. noxious
d. welcome

10. traumatic
a. dangerous
b. trustworthy
c. soothing
d. sage

11. abortive
a. consummated
b. untimely
c. idealistic
d. reveling

12. bilious
a. delightful
b. peevish
c. punctual
d. impoverished

13. iconoclastic
a. rational
b. conservative
c. decisive
d. aggressive

14. corollary
a. instrument
b. eve
c. axiom
d. malapropism

15. obloquy
a. confusion
b. acclaim
c. vilification
d. clarify

16. prurient
a. prudish
b. salacious
c. tiresome
d. polluted

Completing the Sentence

From the following lists of words, choose the one that best completes each of the following sentences. Write the word in the space provided.

aficionado	cognate	emolument	modulates
bruit	elixir	in medias res	vicissitude

1. You have no right to change the rules _____ just because you're losing!

2. Though modern "alchemists" continue the age-old search for the putative _____ of life, I don't think any such nostrum exists.

3. The process of growing up often _____ the intensity of our reactions to things we like or dislike.

4. Unfortunately, the _____ of a college professor is almost always considerably lower than that of an executive in the business world.

5. A true _____ of baseball can reel off the batting average of every member of the Hall of Fame.

Word Families

A. *On the line provided, write the word you have learned in Units 4–6 that is related to each of the following nouns.*
EXAMPLE: biliousness—**bilious**

1. iconoclast, iconoclasm, icon _____

2. prurience, pruriency _____

3. tendentiousness _____

4. saturnalia _____

5. symptom _____

6. immurement _____

7. modulation, modulator, modulability _____

8. ineffableness, ineffability _____

9. insouciance _____

10. wag, waggishness, waggery _____

11. maladroitness _____

12. portent, portentousness _____

13. system, systemization, systematizer, systematist _____

14. risibility _____

B. *On the line provided, write the word you have learned in Units 4–6 that is related to each of the following verbs.*

EXAMPLE: divine—**divination**

15. systematize, systemize _____

16. dictate _____

17. personify, personate, impersonate _____

18. portend _____

19. traumatize _____

20. abort _____

Two-Word Completions

Circle the pair of words that best complete the meaning of each of the following passages.

1. Though I can't say that I relish the thriller as a literary form, I'm a real _____ of the detective _____.

a. pundit . . . touchstone
b. iconoclast . . . matrix
c. aficionado . . . genre
d. persona . . . folderol

2. In one of her more devastating _____, Dorothy Parker is reputed to have once observed that an incompetent actor's interpretation of a role ran the _____ of emotions from A to B.

a. dicta . . . gamut
b. lucubrations . . . mnemonic
c. corollaries . . . cul-de-sac
d. homilies . . . parameters

3. Famous for his daring _____ deep behind Northern lines, J. E. B. Stuart, the South's most colorful cavalry commander, led his men on one dangerous mission after another with all the _____ and style of one of Charlemagne's legendary paladins.

a. obsequies . . . persona
b. emoluments . . . prescience
c. philippics . . . derring-do
d. forays . . . panache

4. When he realized that flattery was getting him nowhere, he attempted to _____ me into acquiescence; but, here again, his efforts proved _____.

a. bruit . . . risible
b. browbeat . . . abortive
c. vitiate . . . tendentious
d. modulate . . . maladroit

gen— race, kind, class; origin, birth

Building with Classical Roots

This root appears in **genre**, "a type, class, or variety, especially with relation to literary composition or painting" (page 59). Some other words based on the same root are listed below.

carcinogen	**degenerate**	**generic**	**genocide**
congenital	**genealogy**	**genesis**	**homogeneous**

From the list of words above, choose the one that corresponds to each of the brief definitions below. Write the word in the blank space in the illustrative sentence below the definition.

1. creation, origin; the coming into being of something

No one is entirely sure of the _____ of the idea that became the Internet we know today.

2. to deteriorate or decline physically or morally; exhibiting such decline; a morally degraded person

The judge condemned their _____ behavior by imposing a stiff sentence.

3. uniform in composition; like in nature or kind

The Latin Club is comprised of a remarkably _____ group of students.

4. relating to an entire group or class; not protected by trademark, nonproprietary

We know many products by their brands but not by their _____ names.

5. cancer-causing substance

Food additives cannot be used unless they pass tests proving that they are not

_____.

6. existing at birth; constituting an essential characteristic as if by birth, inherent

No amount of guidance and counseling could overcome the fact that she was simply a _____ liar.

7. a record or account of a family's or a person's descent; lineage; the study of ancestry and family histories

Using on-line resources, he was able to trace his _____ back ten generations.

8. the systematic extermination of a racial, political, or cultural group

During the regime of Pol Pot (1975–1979), Khmer Rouge forces in Cambodia conducted a _____ of unprecedented proportions.

From the list of words on page 79, choose the one that best completes each of the following sentences. Write the word in the blank space provided.

1. Rather than specify a particular brand, many physicians now prescribe less expensive _____ drugs for their patients.

2. The _____ of Herman Melville's masterpiece *Moby Dick* lay in the author's experiences as a seaman aboard a whaling vessel.

3. The debate, which had begun as a high-minded and civil exchange of views, rapidly _____ into an ugly, name-calling brawl.

4. When I stumbled across an old family _____, I discovered that I am descended from a veteran of the Revolutionary War.

5. Consumer groups petitioned the government to ban the pesticide when it was discovered to contain a proven _____.

6. The argument boiled down to a dispute over how much of one's character is _____ and how much is acquired.

7. The designers had carefully coordinated the wallpaper, upholstery, drapes, and accessories to lend the room a _____ appearance.

8. Tribal leaders branded the regime's plan to "relocate" the remaining native population as tantamount to _____.

---

*Circle the **boldface** word that more satisfactorily completes each of the following sentences.*

1. Asbestos, once commonly used in building construction and insulation and in making fireproof textiles, is now recognized as a powerful (**genocide, carcinogen**) and health hazard.

2. Olympic athlete Flo Hyman died at the age of 31 of a (**congenital, generic**) disorder known as Marfan syndrome.

3. An old seventeenth-century English saying compares a (**homogeneous, degenerate**) nobleman to a turnip because the only good in them is found underground.

4. Because so many records were destroyed during the Holocaust, many people with European Jewish roots remain thwarted in their efforts to compile a thorough (**genealogy, genesis**).

5. Humorist Erma Bombeck wrote that " . . . 'mother' has always been a (**degenerate, generic**) term synonymous with love, devotion, and sacrifice."

6. In Rwanda in 1994, the Hutu tried to eliminate the Tutsi in brutal (**genocide, genealogy**).

7. Some schools assign students to (**homogeneous, congenital**) classes in the belief that such groupings provide the best environment for steady progress.

8. The science of physical optics explores and analyzes the (**carcinogen, genesis**), nature, and properties of light.

Analogies

In each of the following, circle the item that best completes the comparison.

1. tearjerker is to **maudlin** as
a. opera is to prurient
b. tragedy is to risible
c. farce is to hilarious
d. satire is to heartrending

2. microcosm is to **macrocosm** as
a. plethora is to paucity
b. poltroon is to craven
c. purview is to orbit
d. parameter is to touchstone

3. salubrious is to **health** as
a. pragmatic is to validity
b. eleemosynary is to profit
c. tendentious is to justice
d. therapeutic is to recovery

4. waggish is to **laughs** as
a. risible is to yawns
b. bilious is to smiles
c. lachrymose is to tears
d. ribald is to sneers

5. philippic is to **vituperative** as
a. liturgy is to ribald
b. encomium is to complimentary
c. harangue is to restrained
d. paean is to scurrilous

6. homily is to **church** as
a. sermon is to air show
b. diatribe is to game show
c. aria is to horse show
d. monologue is to talk show

7. diaphanous is to **veils** as
a. noisome is to clouds
b. gossamer is to cobwebs
c. bulky is to showers
d. abortive is to breezes

8. klutz is to **maladroit** as
a. bigot is to intolerant
b. dynamo is to supine
c. aficionado is to blasé
d. pundit is to ignorant

9. mnemonic is to **memory** as
a. trousers are to speech
b. glasses are to vision
c. earmuffs are to movement
d. blinders are to hearing

10. insouciant is to **concern** as
a. oblivious is to consciousness
b. sanguine is to optimism
c. quizzical is to erudition
d. portentous is to intrepidity

Choosing the Right Meaning

Read each sentence carefully. Then circle the item that best completes the statement below the sentence.

"My brother, who despairs of ever changing our parents' hidebound views, has given up dinner-table discussions aimed at convincing them to adopt more liberal attitudes. (2)

1. In line 1 the word **hidebound** is used to mean
a. narrow-minded   b. free-wheeling   c. ribald   d. pragmatic

"These late eclipses in the sun and moon portend no good to us. Though the wisdom of nature can reason thus and thus, yet nature finds itself scourged by the sequent effects." (2)
      (Shakespeare, *King Lear*, I, ii, 103–106)

2. The word **portend** in line 1 most nearly means
a. inspire awe   b. offer   c. forebode   d. conjure

Herman Melville's masterpiece *Moby Dick* is prefaced by a sort of lexicon of etymological entries and quoted passages having to do with whales and whaling. (2)

3. The best definition for the word **lexicon** in line 1 is

a. glossary   b. dictionary   c. wordbook   d. compendium

I will grant that manners and mores may change with the times, but common courtesy is never effete. (2)

4. In line 2 the word **effete** is used to mean

a. exhausted   b. sterile   c. out-of-date   d. enfeebled

One of the great masters of genre painting is the Dutch artist Jan Vermeer, whose depictions of everyday scenes seem magically infused with light and life. (2)

5. The word **genre** in line 1 most nearly means

a. still life   b. realist   c. abstract   d. category

Two-Word Completions

Circle the pair of words that best complete the meaning of each of the following sentences.

1. In Gaetano Donizetti's famous comic opera *The* _____ *of Love*, a clever charlatan _____ an overly gullible country bumpkin into believing that a plain old bottle of Bordeaux wine is in fact a powerful love potion that will solve the poor yokel's amorous problems overnight.

a. *Mnemonic* . . . apprises
b. *Elixir* . . . cozens

c. *Parameter* . . . browbeats
d. *Vassal* . . . forays

2. Prudish Victorians were so offended by the _____ jokes and salacious language in some of Shakespeare's plays that they would only read his works in heavily _____ versions.

a. prurient . . . polarized
b. risible . . . vitiated

c. ribald . . . bowdlerized
d. ineffable . . . deracinated

3. The _____ of the forty _____ contained in *Sketches of Country Life* is truly extraordinary, and the reader is left with the distinct impression that he or she actually knows the people who are being described.

a. poltroonery . . . enclaves
b. verisimilitude . . . vignettes

c. rapacity . . . paeans
d. virtuosity . . . claques

4. Recently, many Christian denominations have modernized the language of the _____ that they use in their service because it had become clear that the presence of obsolete words and phrases in the traditional material tended to _____ the meaning of the rites for contemporary congregations.

a. homilies . . . bowdlerize
b. obsequies . . . bruit

c. lucubrations . . . vitiate
d. liturgies . . . obfuscate

Enriching Your Vocabulary

Read the passage below. Then complete the exercise at the bottom of the page.

What's in a Name?

When you don a cardigan sweater, it's unlikely that you salute James Thomas Brudenell, Seventh Earl of Cardigan (1797–1868). That British officer's title describes a style of collarless long-sleeved sweater that opens in front. Cardigan's troops wore this garment during the Crimean War. The noun "cardigan" is an example of an *eponym*—a word derived from the name of the person originally associated with the object, practice, or attitude that the word indicates.

Many eponymns enrich the English language. One example is *bowdlerize* (Unit 3). This eponym, as you may recall, comes from the name of the nineteenth century English editor who published an edition of the works of William Shakespeare in which "those words [were] omitted which [could not] with propriety be read aloud in a family." Over time, the origins of eponyms may fade from common knowledge. Did you know that graham crackers are named for Sylvester Graham, an American nutritionist who promoted the use of whole-grain flour? French acrobat Jules Leotard, the subject of the song "The Man on the Flying Trapeze," designed a tight-fitting yet flexible garment that showed off his muscles. Adolphe Sax, a Belgian instrument maker, combined the reed of a clarinet with the fingering of an oboe to form the saxophone, the instrument that bears his name to this day.

The snug-fitting leotard was designed to provide unlimited freedom of movement.

In Column A below are 8 more eponyms. With or without a dictionary, match each word with its meaning in Column B.

Column A

_____ **1.** boycott
_____ **2.** gerrymander
_____ **3.** lynch
_____ **4.** maverick
_____ **5.** quisling
_____ **6.** sandwich
_____ **7.** shrapnel
_____ **8.** sideburns

Column B

a. a traitor, turncoat or collaborator with an enemy

b. to execute illegally, usually by hanging

c. a fragment from a bomb, mine, or shell

d. to divide a region into oddly shaped electoral districts to give one party unfair advantage during an election

e. a nonconformist or dissenter

f. hair grown in front of the ears

g. to refuse to buy, use, or deal with as a way to force the acceptance of some form of behavior; a protest

h. two slices of bread with meat or other filling between them

Definitions

Note carefully the spelling, pronunciation, part(s) of speech, and definition(s) of each of the following words. Then write the word in the blank space(s) in the illustrative sentence(s) following. Finally, study the lists of synonyms and antonyms given at the end of each entry.

1. abeyance
(ə bā′ əns)

(*n.*) a state of being temporarily inactive, suspended, or set aside

The administrators and staff reluctantly agreed to hold the matter in _____.

SYNONYMS: deferment, postponement, suspension

2. ambivalent
(am biv′ ə lənt)

(*adj.*) having opposite and conflicting feelings about someone or something

Despite their deeply _____ attitudes, the scientists went ahead with the program.

SYNONYMS: equivocal, ambiguous, of two minds
ANTONYMS: unequivocal, unambiguous, clear-cut

3. beleaguer
(bi lē′ gər)

(*v.*) to set upon from all sides; to surround with an army; to trouble, harass

Sherman's division arrived by train, then positioned itself to _____ the city's fortress.

SYNONYMS: besiege, encircle, pester

4. carte blanche
(kärt′ blänsh′)

(*n.*) full freedom or authority to act at one's own discretion

The boss gave us _____ in the matter of how we were going to approach the client.

SYNONYMS: blank check, free rein

5. cataclysm
(kat′ ə kliz əm)

(*n.*) a sudden, violent, or devastating upheaval; a surging flood, deluge

Diplomacy could not stop the _____ of World War I.

SYNONYMS: disaster, catastrophe

6. debauch
(di bôch′)

(*v.*) to corrupt morally, seduce; to indulge in dissipation; (*n.*) an act or occasion of dissipation or vice

Those who would _____ the innocent deserve our wrath.

The _____ began at midnight.

SYNONYMS: (*v.*) carouse, (*n.*) spree, orgy
ANTONYMS: (*v.*) elevate, uplift, inspire, purify

7. éclat
(ā klä')

(*n.*) dazzling or conspicuous success or acclaim; great brilliance (of performance or achievement)

Dazzled by the _____ of the performance, critics heaped praise on the troupe.

SYNONYM: celebrity
ANTONYMS: dullness, insipidity, mediocrity

8. fastidious
(fa stid' ē əs)

(*adj.*) overly demanding or hard to please; excessively careful in regard to details; easily disgusted

Known for her _____ taste, the decorator was always in great demand.

SYNONYMS: precise, meticulous, exacting, finicky
ANTONYMS: careless, sloppy, messy, untidy, slovenly

9. gambol
(gam' bəl)

(*v.*) to jump or skip about playfully

The children began to _____ like fawns in a meadow.

SYNONYMS: frolic, romp, cavort, caper
ANTONYMS: lumber, trudge, plod

10. imbue
(im byü')

(*v.*) to soak or stain thoroughly; to fill the mind

The celebrated teacher strove to _____ her students with the desire to succeed.

SYNONYMS: infuse, instill, inculcate
ANTONYMS: remove, expunge, eradicate, erase

11. inchoate
(in kō' it)

(*adj.*) just beginning; not fully shaped or formed

At first a molten and _____ mass, it soon grew, picked up speed, and destroyed all in its path.

SYNONYMS: incipient, embryonic, rudimentary
ANTONYMS: mature, developed, complete

12. lampoon
(lam pün')

(*n.*) a malicious satire; (*v.*) to satirize, ridicule

Their _____ of his speech impediment did not amuse the dictator.

The intent was to _____ the senator.

SYNONYMS: (*n.*) burlesque; (*v.*) parody
ANTONYMS: (*n.*) compliment, flattery, homage

13. malleable
(mal' ē ə bəl)

(*adj.*) capable of being formed into different shapes; capable of being altered, adapted, or influenced

The _____ minds of the young students were at the mercy of the charismatic professor.

SYNONYMS: pliable, impressionable, adaptable
ANTONYMS: rigid, inflexible, unyielding, intractable

14. nemesis
(nem′ ə sis)

(*n.*) an agent or force inflicting vengeance or punishment; retribution itself; an unbeatable rival

Calculus proved to be my _____.

SYNONYMS: comeuppance, avenger
ANTONYMS: guardian angel, ally, patron

15. opt
(opt)

(*v.*) to make a choice or decision

We decided to _____ for the cheaper model.

SYNONYMS: choose, select, decide

16. philistine
(fil′ i stēn)

(*adj.*) lacking in, hostile to, or smugly indifferent to cultural and artistic values or refinements; (*n.*) such a person

Their _____ contempt for art is something the curator simply cannot abide.

The mayor is seen as a _____ by the members of the city's arts community.

SYNONYMS: (*adj.*) boorish, lowbrow; (*n.*) yahoo
ANTONYMS: (*adj.*) refined, cultivated; (*n.*) esthete, highbrow

17. picaresque
(pik ə resk′)

(*adj.*) involving or characteristic of clever rogues or adventurers

Reviewers cited the _____ element in the novel as its best feature.

SYNONYMS: roguish, rascally, rakish

18. queasy
(kwē′ zē)

(*adj.*) nauseated or uneasy; causing nausea or uneasiness; troubled

The remarks gave me a _____ feeling in the pit of my stomach.

SYNONYM: unsettled
ANTONYMS: calm, untroubled, confident

19. refractory
(ri frak′ tə rē)

(*adj.*) stubborn; hard or difficult to manage; not responsive to treatment or cure

Caring for the _____ patient left us exhausted and drained.

SYNONYMS: unruly, disobedient, willful, mulish
ANTONYMS: docile, tractable, dutiful, obedient

20. savoir-faire
(sav wär fâr′)

(*n.*) the ability to say and do the right thing in any situation; social competence

The experienced and wily ambassador handled the delicate affair with her usual _____.

SYNONYMS: tact, finesse, suavity, sophistication
ANTONYMS: tactlessness, gaucherie, boorishness

Completing the Sentence

From the words for this unit, choose the one that best completes each of the following sentences. Write the word in the space provided.

1. You made some rather clever suggestions at the meeting, but on the whole your ideas were far too _____ to serve as the basis for a workable plan.

2. Perhaps once in a generation, a people is faced with a great moral crisis in which it must _____ for good or evil, war or peace, life or death.

3. Oscar's careless housekeeping and sloppy habits were an endless source of exasperation to his _____ roommate.

4. Should we expect the needs and purposes of a true poet to be understood by such a thoroughgoing _____?

5. Instead of settling down to a job and a family, Tom seems to be modeling his life on the career of some rogue out of a(n) _____ novel.

6. How could they have _____ themselves by joining in that obscene celebration?

7. Such capacity for growth and self-improvement can be expected only in the _____ years of the teens and early twenties.

8. I was confident that I would do well in the scholarship examination, but my hopes were dashed by my old _____, mathematics.

9. Many scientists are fearful that the West Coast may someday suffer a(n) _____ as violent as the earthquake that devastated San Francisco in 1906.

10. Her equivocal answers to my questions about going to college in the fall clearly revealed her _____ attitude toward leaving home.

11. There are circumstances under which it is desirable to make decisions swiftly and unequivocally, but there are other cases in which it is wise to hold decisions in _____.

12. Though Jane's mount was as docile as a newborn lamb, mine proved to be the most _____ animal I had ever ridden.

13. A host of creditors _____ the hapless businessman with demands for payment and threats of legal action.

14. Since I had unlimited faith in their honesty and discretion, I felt no qualms about giving them _____ to do whatever they thought was necessary.

15. The purpose of the course in American history is to _____ young people with a genuine understanding and appreciation of what this country stands for.

16. The entire issue of the magazine was designed as a(n) _____ satirizing the follies and futilities of mass-consumption advertising.

17. The young pianist dazzled the audience with the _____ and verve of his performance.

Unit 7 ■ 87

18. As we turned in to the ranch, we saw two young colts _____ playfully in the open field.

19. I freely confess that just the sight of a roller coaster is enough to make me feel

_____ .

20. They showed such a deplorable lack of _____ in handling that difficult situation that they converted a mere unpleasantness into a social disaster.

 **Synonyms**

Choose the word from this unit that is **the same** or **most nearly the same** in meaning as the **boldface** word or expression in the given phrase. Write the word on the line provided.

1. found the audience to be **impressionable** _____

2. was in its **rudimentary** form at that time _____

3. welcomed the **deferment** _____

4. did not participate in the **spree** _____

5. **instill** the troops with courage _____

6. a **catastrophe** never to be forgotten _____

7. a **roguish** novel of epic adventures _____

8. proceeded to **ridicule** the speaker _____

9. offered us **free rein** _____

10. **harass** the messenger of the bad news _____

11. took power with **acclaim** _____

12. **choose** for us to study abroad _____

13. dresses in a **meticulous** manner _____

14. an **equivocal** response _____

15. unappreciated by the crowd of **yahoos** _____

 **Antonyms**

Choose the word from this unit that is **most nearly opposite** in meaning to the **boldface** word or expression in the given phrase. Write the word on the line provided.

16. approached by our **ally** _____

17. is a **dutiful** employee _____

18. gives me a **confident** feeling _____

19. known for their **tactlessness** _____

20. asked to **trudge** across the stage _____

Choosing the Right Word

Circle the **boldface** word that more satisfactorily completes each of the following sentences.

1. In spite of his courage and love of adventure, he lacks the stature of a true hero; his character might better be described as (**picaresque, abeyant**).

2. Although his poetry is somewhat crude and (**inchoate, fastidious**), it has a primitive energy and drive that many readers find extremely attractive.

3. Instead of endless lamentations about how bad things are, let us try to look realistically at the (**lampoons, options**) open to us.

4. James Thurber's stories are extremely funny, but they are also (**imbued, debauched**) with a profound sense of the pathos of the human condition.

5. Because Thurber combines humor and pathos so masterfully, we might say that the mood of his stories is (**malleable, ambivalent**).

6. Their obsession with military conquest, leading them to waste their vast resources on armaments and endless wars, proved to be their (**nemesis, gambol**).

7. Another world war would be a(n) (**éclat, cataclysm**) on so vast a scale that it is doubtful whether civilization could survive it.

8. He will never realize his full athletic potential as long as he remains (**beleaguered, opted**) by doubts about his own ability.

9. Would it not be a gross miscarriage of justice to prosecute us under a law which, for all practical purposes, has been in (**abeyance, carte blanche**) since the early years of the last century?

10. With all the misplaced confidence of inexperienced youth, I set out to make a million dollars by (**gamboling, imbuing**) in the not-so-verdant pastures of Wall Street.

11. Perhaps she felt disturbed at the prospect of having to betray her friends, but she seems to have overcome her (**queasiness, éclat**) without too much trouble.

12. Since they had always been reasonably well-behaved, I was utterly taken aback by their (**ambivalent, refractory**) behavior.

13. She was completely bewildered by the exhibition of abstract art, but, fearing to be labeled a (**lampoon, philistine**), she pretended to understand what she was looking at.

14. Perhaps you hope to divert our attention from your own misconduct by maliciously (**lampooning, gamboling**) a sincere and able public official.

15. Their (**fastidious, ambivalent**) preoccupation with minor details of style is not to be confused with a genuine feeling for language.

16. It is one thing to be open-minded and (**queasy, malleable**); it is quite another to be without fixed ideas or principles of any kind.

17. Refusing to become flustered, she handled the embarrassing situation with the finesse and (**queasiness, savoir-faire**) of a born diplomat.

18. Although we disagreed with much that you said, we could not help admiring the rhetorical brilliance and (**cataclysm, éclat**) of your writing style.

19. With plenty of free time and with an excellent library at my disposal, I gave myself up to a delightful (**cataclysm, debauch**) of reading.

20. In the last analysis all lines of authority and responsibility lead back to the President; he cannot give (**carte blanche, nemesis**) to any assistant.

Vocabulary in Context

*Read the following passage, in which some of the words you have studied in this unit appear in **boldface** type. Then complete each statement given below the passage by circling the letter of the item that is **the same** or **almost the same** in meaning as the highlighted word.*

A Lifelong Reformer

(Line)

The women's rights movement was an **inchoate** association of reformers when, in 1848, Elizabeth Cady Stanton (1815–1902) helped to organize the Seneca Falls Convention. A driving force behind that first women's rights convention, Stanton became the first to publicly demand the vote for women.

Stanton, who received a top-notch education at Emma Willard's Academy in Troy, (5) New York, could have chosen a life of social and leisure activities. But, instead, she married the abolitionist Henry B. Stanton, and **opted for** a life of politics and reform.

In 1851, Stanton met and formed a lifelong partnership with Susan B. Anthony, another aggressive worker for abolition and women's rights. During the Civil War, Stanton considered putting women's rights agitation in **abeyance**. But neither she nor (10)

A determined woman's heritage: A young woman registers to vote.

Anthony could stay inactive. They formed the National Women's Loyal League to demand the abolition of slavery. Both were disappointed when, after the war, women were still not given (15) the right to vote.

Undaunted, Stanton worked tirelessly to get legislation passed on behalf of women and to **imbue** all women with the desire for equal (20) treatment under the law. In 1869, she and Anthony founded the National Woman Suffrage Association. In 1876, she convinced a senator to introduce a woman suffrage amendment. This amendment was finally passed in 1920. (25)

But Elizabeth Cady Stanton's interests went far beyond fighting for the right to vote. In fact, she was **beleaguered** for her views on other women's rights issues, as well as several other controversies current at the time. These views hurt her standing in the women's movement, but never for a moment slowed her work on behalf of civil rights for women. (30)

---

1. The meaning of **inchoate** (line 1) is
a. unstable
b. impressive
c. ambivalent
d. embryonic

2. Opted for (line 7) most nearly means
a. rejected
b. chose
c. neglected
d. requested

3. Abeyance (line 10) is best defined as
a. acclaim
b. parody
c. suspension
d. ambiguity

4. The meaning of **imbue** (line 19) is
a. infuse
b. expunge
c. paint
d. see

5. Beleaguered (line 27) most nearly means
a. beloved
b. flattered
c. harassed
d. corrupted

Definitions

Note carefully the spelling, pronunciation, part(s) of speech, and definition(s) of each of the following words. Then write the word in the blank space(s) in the illustrative sentence(s) following. Finally, study the lists of synonyms and antonyms given at the end of each entry.

1. aberration
(ab ə rā′ shən)

(*n.*) a departure from what is proper, right, expected, or normal; a lapse from a sound mental state

In an _____ of judgment, the coach chose not to call a critical time-out.

SYNONYMS: deviation, anomaly, irregularity

2. ad hoc
(ad′ häk′)

(*adj.*) for this specific purpose; improvised; (*adv.*) with respect to this

An _____ committee was formed immediately.

We met, _____, to consider the issue.

SYNONYM: (*adj.*) makeshift
ANTONYMS: (*adj.*) permanent, long-standing

3. bane
(bān)

(*n.*) the source or cause of fatal injury, death, destruction, or ruin; death or ruin itself; poison

Rain, the _____ of picnics, was forecast for the day we had scheduled ours.

SYNONYMS: spoiler, bête noire
ANTONYMS: blessing, comfort, solace, balm

4. bathos
(bā′ thos)

(*n.*) the intrusion of commonplace or trite material into a context whose tone is lofty or elevated; grossly insincere or exaggerated sentimentality; the lowest phase, nadir; an anticlimax, comedown

After wallowing in _____, the writer returned to her novel in earnest.

SYNONYMS: mawkishness, mush, schmaltz

5. cantankerous
(kan taŋ′ kə rəs)

(*adj.*) ill-tempered, quarrelsome; difficult to get along or deal with

The _____ machine befuddled the team of technicians assigned to repair it.

SYNONYMS: cranky, testy, peevish, irascible, ornery
ANTONYMS: good-natured, sweet-tempered, genial

6. casuistry
(kazh′ ū is trē)

(*n.*) the determination of right and wrong in questions of conduct or conscience by the application of general ethical principles; specious argument

The professor's ideas, once highly regarded, now appear to be nothing more than ingenious _____.

SYNONYMS: sophistry, quibbling

7. de facto
(dē fak′ tō)

(*adj.*) actually existing or in effect, although not legally required or sanctioned; (*adv.*) in reality, actually

The dictator's wife is the _____ head of state.

It appears that, _____ , the information is true.

SYNONYMS: in actuality, in point of fact
ANTONYMS: de jure, by right

8. depredation
(dep rə dā′ shən)

(*n.*) the act of preying upon or plundering

The _____ of the invaders left scars that will take years to heal.

SYNONYMS: looting, pillage, outrage

9. empathy
(em′ pə thē)

(*n.*) a sympathetic understanding of or identification with the feelings, thoughts, or attitudes of someone or something else

The grandparents felt _____ for the aspirations of their grandchildren.

SYNONYMS: sympathy, compassion
ANTONYMS: insensitivity, callousness, detachment

10. harbinger
(här′ bən jər)

(*n.*) a forerunner, herald; (*v.*) to herald the approach of

Daffodils in bloom are a _____ of spring.

Crocuses, too, _____ the approach of spring.

SYNONYMS: (*n.*) precursor; (*v.*) presage
ANTONYMS: (*n.*) aftermath, epilogue, sequel

11. hedonism
(hē′ də niz əm)

(*n.*) the belief that the attainment of pleasure is life's chief aim; devotion to or pursuit of pleasure

A beach bum's mindless _____ may appeal to all working people at one time or another.

SYNONYMS: pleasure seeking, sensuality, sybaritism
ANTONYMS: asceticism, puritanism, self-denial

12. lackluster
(lak′ lus tər)

(*adj.*) lacking brilliance or vitality; dull

The weary soldier's _____ stare haunted the photographer, who captured it with her lens.

SYNONYMS: vapid, insipid, drab, flat
ANTONYMS: brilliant, radiant, dazzling

13. malcontent
(mal′ kən tent)

(*adj.*) discontented with or in open defiance of prevailing conditions; (*n.*) such a person

The _____ transit workers went out on strike.

The angry mayor referred to the strikers as a group of vocal, lazy _____ .

SYNONYMS: (*adj.*) dissatisfied, disgruntled; (*n.*) grumbler
ANTONYMS: (*adj.*) satisfied, contented, complacent, smug

14. mellifluous
(mə lif′ lü əs)

(*adj.*) flowing sweetly or smoothly; honeyed

The folk singer's _____ voice appealed to young and old the world over.

SYNONYMS: euphonious, musical
ANTONYMS: shrill, strident, harsh, grating

15. nepotism
(nep′ ə tiz əm)

(*n.*) undue favoritism to or excessive patronage of one's relatives

To avoid any hint of _____, the owner of the team refused to hire any of his relatives.

16. pander
(pan′ dər)

(*v.*) to cater to or provide satisfaction for the low tastes or vices of others; (*n.*) a person who does this

The hosts proceeded to _____ to the every whim of their delighted guests.

The friend acted as a _____, ferrying secret messages back and forth between them.

SYNONYMS: (*v.*) indulge; (*n.*) pimp, procurer

17. peccadillo
(pek ə dil′ ō)

(*n.*) a minor sin or offense; a trifling fault or shortcoming

If you will overlook my _____, I will ignore yours.

SYNONYM: indiscretion
ANTONYMS: felony, mortal sin, enormity, atrocity

18. pièce de résistance
(pē əs də rā zē stäns′)

(*n.*) the principal dish of a meal; the principal event, incident, or item; an outstanding accomplishment

The _____ of the remarkable repast was the dessert, a ten-tiered cake adorned with spun sugar.

SYNONYMS: centerpiece, chef d'oeuvre
ANTONYMS: preliminary, hors d'oeuvre

19. remand
(ri mand′)

(*v.*) to send or order back; in law, to send back to jail or to a lower court

The outlaw was _____ to the custody of the sheriff.

SYNONYMS: remit, return
ANTONYMS: forward to, send on, release

20. syndrome
(sin′ drōm)

(*n.*) a group of symptoms or signs that collectively characterize or indicate a disease, disorder, abnormality, etc.

With ubiquitous computer use, carpal tunnel has become a decidedly modern _____.

SYNONYMS: complex, pattern

Completing the Sentence

From the words for this unit, choose the one that best completes each of the following sentences. Write the word in the space provided.

1. The pitcher's lightning fastball has proved the _____ of many a celebrated home-run hitter.

2. Her visits to the nursing home are motivated not by a detached sense of duty but by a genuine _____ for those who are lonely.

3. Like everyone else, I was charmed by the _____ tones of the speaker, but afterwards I could extract very little real meaning from what she said.

4. How is one to explain that strange _____ from the habits and standards which he had followed for so many years?

5. I think you are showing poor judgment in condemning them so severely for what is, after all, little more than a(n) _____ .

6. Since there was no agency concerned with race relations, the Mayor created a(n) _____ committee to deal with such matters.

7. Those cases that call for further attention will be _____ to the proper agencies.

8. It was hard to believe that the eager, vibrant youth I had known was now this shabby derelict, staring into space with _____ eyes.

9. A high temperature, yellowish complexion, and general feeling of fatigue are all characteristic of the mononucleosis _____ .

10. He had been happy-go-lucky as a young man, but years of disappointment and misfortune have turned him sour and _____ .

11. Would it be ungracious of me to suggest that the _____ of the feast, given on the menu as "filet mignon," had the taste and texture of old shoe leather?

12. Yes, I believe in helping out relatives, but I haven't spent a lifetime building this business to make it a monument to _____ .

13. Since they have followed a policy of bringing in executives and supervisors from the outside, instead of promoting from within their own ranks, the office is filled with grumbling _____ .

14. Though he had embraced a creed of unabashed _____ in his youth, he ended his life among a group of ascetics living in the desert.

15. Is it too optimistic to hope that your willingness to undertake that thankless task is the _____ of a new maturity and a more responsible attitude?

16. Those sentimentalized effusions introduced a note of _____ into what should have been an occasion marked by dignity and restraint.

17. Yes, you have scored a quick commercial success, but you have done it only by _____ to low and depraved tastes.

18. I find myself in the position of a(n) _____ supervisor; now I would like to have the title, salary, and privileges that go along with the job.

19. The history of Nazi Germany and Fascist Italy teaches us that we should never let ourselves be blinded by the meretricious _____ of a demagogue, no matter how appealing it may appear at first glance.

20. It took years for that country to recover from the _____ wrought by the Second World War and its concomitant social and economic dislocations.

Synonyms

*Choose the word from this unit that is **the same** or **most nearly the same** in meaning as the **boldface** word or expression in the given phrase. Write the word on the line provided.*

1. a **cranky** schoolmaster _____

2. serves, **in actuality**, as the chef _____

3. is a **herald** of the coming of winter _____

4. warm weather, the **bête noire** of ski resorts _____

5. struck me as utter **sophistry** _____

6. victims of the **pillage** _____

7. dismissed as **schmaltz** by critics _____

8. seen by scientists as an **anomaly** _____

9. the **centerpiece** of the meal _____

10. committed several **indiscretions** _____

11. **return** them to their grandparents' care _____

12. refuses to **cater** to the criminal element _____

13. charged with **favoritism** by his opponents _____

14. completely without **compassion** _____

15. suffers from a recognizable **group of symptoms** _____

Antonyms

*Choose the word from this unit that is **most nearly opposite** in meaning to the **boldface** word or expression in the given phrase. Write the word on the line provided.*

16. always wears a **contented** expression _____

17. never experienced **self-denial** _____

18. awakened by the **shrill** sound _____

19. the **long-standing** team of economists _____

20. their **dazzling** performance in the key game _____

Choosing the Right Word

*Circle the **boldface** word that more satisfactorily completes each of the following sentences.*

1. Said Churchill to the British people after the Munich agreement: "We must reject these (**mellifluous, malcontent**) assurances of 'peace in our time.'"

2. With the extreme cold and the deep snows still holding on, the gradual lengthening of the days was the only (**aberration, harbinger**) of spring.

3. The negotiators agreed not to try to draw up an overall treaty but to deal with each specific problem on a(n)(**de facto, ad hoc**) basis.

4. Your efforts to prove that because "no one is perfect," all moral standards are relative and therefore meaningless, struck me as sheer (**casuistry, hedonism**).

5. In many respects it is a good movie, but sadly, the director has allowed sentiment to spill over into sentimentality, and sentimentality into (**bathos, casuistry**).

6. True, we won the game, but I think our team gave a rather (**lackluster, malcontent**) performance in beating a weak opponent by so narrow a margin.

7. "Am I to be accused of (**casuistry, nepotism**)," queried the Mayor, "just because my wife, daughter, brother, and nephew happen to be the best applicants for the jobs?"

8. A candidate for high public office should seek to debate the issues on an objective level, instead of (**remanding, pandering**) to the prejudices and misconceptions of the times.

9. The (**aberrations, depredations**) of the terrible disease could be seen only too clearly in her extreme emaciation and feebleness.

10. We learned with dismay that our application had been neither approved nor rejected, but (**pandered, remanded**) to a "higher authority for further consideration."

11. Although the law forbids residential separation of the races, we all know that a state of (**de facto, ad hoc**) segregation exists in some communities.

12. So strong is my (**empathy, casuistry**) with the poems of Robert Frost that I often feel as though I could have written them myself.

13. The car was forever breaking down, but its owner seemed to derive a sort of perverse satisfaction out of battling with the (**mellifluous, cantankerous**) old heap.

14. Then came Miss Bolton's cornet solo, which we all recognized immediately as the (**pièce de résistance, casuistry**) of that long musical evening.

15. We must not assume that their behavior, however (**aberrant, mellifluous**) by conventional standards, is a sign of mental illness.

16. The (**baneful, mellifluous**) looks which they directed at us made it only too clear that we had little hope for mercy at their hands.

17. We may find (**malcontents, hedonists**) annoying, but the fact is that they often serve as "gadflies" to bring about desirable changes.

18. How can you compare a mere social (**peccadillo, depredation**) with a misdeed that has caused such great harm to other people?

19. The (**syndrome, bathos**) of poverty, drug addiction, and crime that afflicts our cities calls for remedial action on a truly national scale.

20. In all aspects of their behavior, they showed the self-indulgence and gross indifference to others that is characteristic of the true (**malcontent, hedonist**).

*Read the following passage, in which some of the words you have studied in this unit appear in **boldface** type. Then complete each statement given below the passage by circling the letter of the item that is **the same** or **almost the same** in meaning as the highlighted word.*

The Great Migration

(Line)

Since the forced resettlement of Africans as slaves in the United States, migration has been a central characteristic of African American life. Before the Civil War, slaves escaped to freedom in the North. During and after it, freed blacks moved to protect their freedom. In the late 1870s, to escape the

(5) **depredations** of the Jim Crow laws, **de facto** and otherwise, more than 50,000 blacks left the South for the Midwest.

But the 1890s witnessed the beginning of the Great Migration—the mass grassroots movement

(10) of blacks from the rural South to the urban North. This lasted until the 1970s; but the single greatest period of migration was during World War I, when Northern factories needed workers desperately. During this time, 500,000 blacks left

(15) the **lackluster** economy of the South for jobs that beckoned. Although the wages they received for these semiskilled jobs were often lower than those of white workers, they were still higher than they were back home. In all, more than 6 million

(20) blacks migrated North between 1916 and 1970.

Although they left behind lynch mobs, disenfranchisement, and few opportunities to improve their quality of life, blacks who came North were not free from the degradations of

(25) racism, the **bane** of their existence. Although many Northerners welcomed their new neighbors with **empathy**, not all did. **Malcontents** started race riots in St. Louis, Chicago, and in other cities.

Jacob Lawrence, *The Migration of the Negro, No. 18: The migration gained in momentum.* Casein tempera on handboard, 18 x 12 in. Museum of Modern Art, New York. Artwork © 2002 Gwendolyn Knight Lawrence, courtesy of The Jacob and Gwendolyn Lawrence Foundation.

(30) Despite all the difficulties they encountered along the way, blacks, in reshaping their lives, have reshaped the United States and the very fabric of American society.

1. The meaning of **depredations** (line 5) is
a. sympathies   c. felonies
b. outrages   d. blessings

2. The meaning of **de facto** (line 5) is
a. actually existing   c. de jure
b. pleasure-seeking   d. by right

3. Lackluster (line 15) most nearly means
a. dazzling   c. flat
b. hedonistic   d. improvised

4. Bane (line 25) most nearly means
a. solace   c. bête noire
b. comfort   d. sophistry

5. Empathy (line 27) is best defined as
a. callousness   c. quibbling
b. favoritism   d. compassion

6. Malcontents (line 28) is best defined as
a. complacent people   c. felons
b. disgruntled people d. smug people

Vocabulary in Context

Unit 8 ■ 97

 **Definitions**

Note carefully the spelling, pronunciation, part(s) of speech, and definition(s) of each of the following words. Then write the word in the blank space(s) in the illustrative sentence(s) following. Finally, study the lists of synonyms and antonyms given at the end of each entry.

1. beatitude
(bē at' ə tüd)

(*n.*) a state of perfect happiness or blessedness; a blessing

Do you think that not having to worry about money is the consummate _____ of being wealthy?

SYNONYMS: bliss, rapture
ANTONYMS: misery, despair

2. bête noire
(bet nwär')

(*n.*) someone or something that one especially dislikes, dreads, or avoids

Spinach used to be the _____ of my diet, but that was before I tasted blood sausage.

SYNONYMS: pet peeve, bugbear, nemesis
ANTONYMS: pet, idol

3. bode
(bōd)

(*v.*) to be an omen of; to indicate by signs

With a smile that _____ good news, the teacher enters the room and greets the students.

SYNONYMS: presage, augur, foreshadow

4. dank
(daŋk)

(*adj.*) unpleasantly damp or wet

The room had the _____ atmosphere of a wet cave.

SYNONYMS: clammy, moist, soggy
ANTONYMS: dry, arid, parched, desiccated

5. ecumenical
(ek yu men' i kəl)

(*adj.*) worldwide or universal in influence or application

An _____ council meets on the third Tuesday of each month.

SYNONYMS: general, comprehensive
ANTONYMS: parochial, regional, insular

6. fervid
(fər' vid)

(*adj.*) burning with enthusiasm or zeal; extremely heated

Using _____ words of praise, the coach gave the team a much-needed pep talk before the big game.

SYNONYMS: ardent, zealous, fervent, earnest
ANTONYMS: apathetic, indifferent, cool, blasé

7. fetid
(fet' id)

(*adj.*) having an unpleasant or offensive odor

The stale, _____ air of the windowless room was an irritation to all who had to be there.

SYNONYMS: smelly, putrid, noisome, foul, malodorous
ANTONYMS: fragrant, aromatic, perfumed, sweet

8. gargantuan
(gär gan' chū ən)

(*adj.*) of immense size, volume, or capacity; enormous, prodigious

The spirited artist had a _____ thirst for life.

SYNONYMS: huge, colossal, mammoth, gigantic
ANTONYMS: tiny, minuscule, infinitesimal, dwarfish

9. heyday
(hā' dā)

(*n.*) the period of greatest power, vigor, success, or influence; the prime years

During the _____ of the clipper ship, these graceful vessels were the swiftest on the seas.

SYNONYM: golden age
ANTONYMS: formative years, twilight years, decline

10. incubus
(in' kyə bəs)

(*n.*) a demon or evil spirit supposed to haunt human beings in their bedrooms at night; anything that oppresses or weighs upon one, like a nightmare

The young child awoke with a loud scream, claiming that a terrifying _____ had entered the room.

SYNONYMS: hobgoblin, millstone, burden

11. infrastructure
(in' frə strək chər)

(*n.*) a basic foundation or framework; a system of public works; the resources and facilities required for an activity; permanent military installations

The city's aging _____ was beginning to become a problem that needed to be addressed.

SYNONYMS: base, basis, underpinning
ANTONYM: superstructure

12. inveigle
(in vā' gəl)

(*v.*) to entice, lure, or snare by flattery or artful inducements; to obtain or acquire by artifice

The planning committee chair _____ us to join them by promising good seats at the ceremony.

SYNONYMS: induce, beguile, cajole, wheedle

13. kudos
(kü' dōs)

(*n.*) the acclaim, prestige, or renown that comes as a result of some action or achievement

The poet received all the _____ due a Nobel laureate.

SYNONYMS: glory, praise, accolades
ANTONYMS: boos, disapproval, condemnation

14. lagniappe
(lan' yap)

(*n.*) an extra or unexpected gift or gratuity

To reward their loyal customers, the grateful store handed out
_____ to all the day's shoppers.

SYNONYM: bonus

15. prolix
(prō lix')

(*adj.*) long-winded and wordy; tending to speak or write in
such a way

The father of the bride regaled anyone who would listen
with a _____ description of the
wedding.

SYNONYMS: verbose, garrulous
ANTONYMS: terse, laconic, succinct, pithy

16. protégé
(prō' tə zhā)

(*n.*) someone whose welfare, training, or career is under the
patronage of an influential person; someone under the
jurisdiction of a foreign country or government

The _____ of the ex-champion
may one day be a champion herself.

SYNONYMS: ward, charge, disciple, trainee
ANTONYMS: sponsor, mentor, benefactor

17. prototype
(prō' tə tīp)

(*n.*) an original pattern or model; a primitive or ancestral form

The _____ of the modern detective
novel is thought to be Poe's "Murders in the Rue Morgue."

SYNONYM: archetype
ANTONYMS: copy, imitation

18. sycophant
(sik' ə fənt)

(*n.*) someone who attempts to win favors or advance him- or
herself by flattery or servile behavior; a slanderer, defamer

The actor, angered by his manager's constant false flattery,
called him a two-faced _____.

SYNONYMS: yes-man, toady, flunky, bootlicker

19. tautology
(tô tol' ə jē)

(*n.*) needless repetition of an idea by using different but
equivalent words; a redundancy

Filled with endless _____ and
solecisms, the lengthy book is a tiresome read.

SYNONYM: pleonasm

20. truckle
(truk' əl)

(*v.*) to yield or submit tamely or submissively

The knight would _____ to no one.

SYNONYMS: kowtow, stoop, grovel
ANTONYMS: resist, defy, stand up to

Completing the Sentence

From the words for this unit, choose the one that best completes each of the following sentences. Write the word in the space provided.

1. As the _____ of one of the great violinists of our times, she has had an unrivaled opportunity to develop her musical talents.

2. The memory of my ghastly blunder and of the harm it had done to innocent people weighed on my spirit like a(n) _____ .

3. Like most people, I enjoy flattery, but I can't be _____ into doing something that in my heart I know is wrong.

4. In the dreamy _____ of their first love, nothing I might have said would have had the slightest effect on them.

5. The speaker emphasized that in the modern world the barriers between different groups are rapidly being broken down and that we must try to think in truly _____ terms.

6. At the risk of losing the election, I refused to _____ to the fleeting passions and prejudices of a small part of the electorate.

7. In *David Copperfield*, Dickens described with heartbreaking realism the period of his own childhood that he spent working as an apprentice in a(n) _____ and chilly cellar.

8. May I say in all modesty that I don't deserve such _____ just because I was all-state in football and led my class academically.

9. I was happy enough when she agreed to go to the prom with me, but her suggestion that we use her car was an unexpected _____ .

10. Was it just our imagination, or was the room still _____ with the smell of stale cigar smoke?

11. Far better to receive sincere criticism, no matter how severe, than the groveling adulation of a(n) _____ .

12. I consider the vogue use of "hopefully" illogical, inept, and pretentious; it has become my linguistic _____ .

13. The atmosphere of distrust and hostility did not _____ well for the outcome of the peace talks.

14. To maintain that because human beings are aggressive animals, they will always be involved in conflicts seems to me a mere _____ .

15. The lame-duck President looked back with nostalgia on the power he had wielded during the _____ of his administration.

16. It was a subject of heated debate in the early nineteenth century whether the federal government should play any part at all in building the _____ to support the fledgling American economy.

17. I think it was terribly naive of us to expect to get a fair hearing from such _____ partisans of the opposing party.

18. After I read one of your _____ and repetitive reports, I always have the feeling that you have never heard the expression "less is more."

19. In H. G. Wells's *The Time Machine*, we see the _____ of a vast number of stories and novels in the area of science fiction.

20. Falstaff is a behemoth of a man, whose _____ appetites, especially for sack and sleep, never seem to be satiated.

Synonyms

*Choose the word from this unit that is **the same** or **most nearly the same** in meaning as the **boldface** word or expression in the given phrase. Write the word on the line provided.*

1. conveyed a sense of **bliss** _____

2. a **putrid** odor from the open cellar door _____

3. abounds in **redundancy** _____

4. the **model** for the house of tomorrow _____

5. a tottering **foundation** _____

6. many attempts to **cajole** them to join _____

7. known throughout the town as a **toady** _____

8. a document of **worldwide** significance _____

9. an unexpected **gratuity** _____

10. **augurs** well for the future of the franchise _____

11. is a **zealous** follower of the guru _____

12. a great champion in her **prime** _____

13. the **burden** of famine and disease _____

14. mud, the **nemesis** of a marching army _____

15. while his **charge** held the sword and shield _____

Antonyms

*Choose the word from this unit that is **most nearly opposite** in meaning to the **boldface** word or expression in the given phrase. Write the word on the line provided.*

16. a **minuscule** portion of food _____

17. wrote a **terse** passage _____

18. **stand up** to the temptation _____

19. the recipient of many **boos** _____

20. descended into the **parched** canyon _____

Choosing the Right Word

Circle the **boldface** word that more satisfactorily completes each of the following sentences.

1. Surrounded from childhood by flattering courtiers, the monarch grew to adulthood unable to distinguish a friend from a (**beatitude, sycophant**).

2. After a long investigation, detectives arrested two con artists who had (**truckled, inveigled**) their many elderly victims into giving them their life savings.

3. His zest for life and his boundless optimism were expressed perfectly, it seemed to me, in his (**gargantuan, fetid**) laughter.

4. Leonardo da Vinci still stands out as the (**prototype, lagniappe**) of the universal genius, equally accomplished in science and in the arts.

5. My criticism of his statement is not merely that it is (**prolix, ecumenical**), but that it uses words to obscure rather than to reinforce the meaning.

6. I have no desire to be known as a nonconformist, but I am not going to allow fear of public disapproval to become my (**beatitude, bête noire**).

7. The lowering clouds and mounting winds did not (**bode, truckle**) well for our hopes for perfect beach weather.

8. When I saw the beautiful girl you had brought to the prom, I understood the reason for your smile of (**fetid, beatific**) self-satisfaction.

9. We can now recognize that many institutions that seemed, at a particular time, to be in their (**incubus, heyday**) were actually already on the decline.

10. You did nothing to help me, but now that I have achieved some success, you have the gall to claim me as your (**protégé, bête noire**).

11. Surely you can make an honest effort to please your employer without (**boding, truckling**) to the vanity of the person who pays your salary.

12. Our goal as a nation and as a society must be to free ourselves completely of the (**sycophant, incubus**) of racial prejudice.

13. When the sanitation strike continued into a second week, people began to complain about the (**fetid, prolix**) smell that hung over the sweltering city.

14. She was such a (**beatific, fervid**) supporter of the Los Angeles Dodgers that she seemed unable to speak of anything else.

15. I felt that I could not continue to live any longer in that (**dank, gargantuan**) atmosphere of prejudice and hostility.

16. I was paid generously for my work, but the kind smile and gracious words were a delightful (**lagniappe, incubus**).

17. In all the great religions, we find common standards that must be regarded as (**fervid, ecumenical**) values, equally valid at all times and in all places.

18. Scientists have for some time been correlating the functions of human consciousness with the neural (**tautology, infrastructure**) of the brain.

19. Her composition was seriously weakened by (**tautologies, kudos**) such as "an older woman who is approaching the end of her life span."

20. In the twilight of her long career, she began to receive the (**heyday, kudos**) that her brilliant but unconventional writings so richly deserved.

*Read the following passage, in which some of the words you have studied in this unit appear in **boldface** type. Then complete each statement given below the passage by circling the letter of the item that is **the same** or **almost the same** in meaning as the highlighted word.*

A True Patriot

(Line)

In the 1770s, American colonists faced a crisis of **gargantuan** proportions—not only were they being taxed without their consent, but British soldiers walked their streets and entered their houses. British spies sat in their taverns and listened in on conversations. Colonial governors clamped down on political activity. The problem was a big one, and to tackle it, groups of **fervid** patriots, such as the Sons of Liberty, (5) met and worked in secret. But the great distances between the villages made communication difficult and concerted action even more so.

For the most part, the leaders of the rebellion were well-heeled, well-educated aristocrats. However, (10) wealth and knowledge were not prerequisites for meaningful participation. Paul Revere, a Boston silversmith, had a typically limited colonial education. But he kept his (15) ear to the ground, and when the time came to act, he did not need to be **inveigled**.

Revere made beautiful teapots, punch bowls, and shoe buckles, but (20) the leaders of the Sons of Liberty

A depiction of Paul Revere's famous midnight ride

knew this stocky tradesman as a patriot who would **truckle** to no one, least of all a British soldier or spy. They also knew that he was a superb rider.

Revere was one of the fastest of the express riders who delivered news to colonial leaders as far away as New York and Philadelphia. This **bête noire** of the (25) English army did not hesitate when his skill was needed most. On the night of April 18, 1775, he used a secret signal and muffled oars to slip past the British warship in Boston Harbor and land at Charlestown, where a horse awaited. Through the countryside he galloped, warning the colonists of the impending arrival of British troops. Paul Revere simply did what had to be done. (30)

---

1. The meaning of **gargantuan** (line 1) is
  a. blissful
  b. mammoth
  c. minuscule
  d. ardent

2. Fervid (line 5) most nearly means
  a. putrid
  b. aromatic
  c. frightened
  d. zealous

3. Inveigled (line 18) is best defined as
  a. asked
  b. paid
  c. cajoled
  d. sponsored

4. The meaning of **truckle** (line 22) is
  a. kowtow
  b. drive
  c. chuckle
  d. stand up

5. Bête noire (line 25) most nearly means
  a. idol
  b. pet
  c. spy
  d. nemesis

Visit us at www.sadlier-oxford.com for interactive puzzles and games.

REVIEW UNITS 7–9

Vocabulary for Comprehension

*Read the following passage, in which some of the words you have studied in Units 7–9 appear in **boldface** type. Then answer questions 1–10 on page 106 on the basis of what is stated or implied in the passage and in the introductory statement.*

This passage describes ancient methods of waste disposal.

(Line)

In a list of the world's significant historical technological advances, one that surely deserves universal support for inclusion is the sewer.
(5) **Kudos** to the ancient engineers who worked on the age-old problem of waste disposal. Imagine if they had not!

Today, an effective sewage system is a key feature of the **infrastructure**
(10) of any city, large or small. But this was not always the case. One of the earliest attempts at a sewage system that improved upon the impractical practice of hauling away waste and
(15) dumping it elsewhere took place about 5,000 years ago in the Orkney Islands, off the coast of Scotland. Archaeologists have discovered evidence of stone-lined drains leading
(20) from small rooms in houses, going underground. These precursors of future sewers emptied into the sea through nearby cliffs.

At about the same time, in the
(25) larger cities of the Indus Valley, engineers were dealing with the same issue, albeit on a grander scale. There, in what is now India and Pakistan, they built networks of
(30) brick drains along the streets. Sewage ran from rooms in houses into underground U-shaped drains.

More than 2,000 years later, sewage disposal methods had
(35) gained little in sophistication. For example, in the **heyday** of the great Athenian civilization, sewage pipes from houses emptied directly into cesspools in the streets. Private
(40) contractors cleaned the foul mess.

Systems improved with the Romans, four centuries later. Emperor Augustus enclosed the massive *Cloaca Maxima*, an
(45) enormous brick sewage tunnel that passed right through the center of the city. This structure, big enough for a chariot to pass through, was one of many the Romans built
(50) throughout their empire. Never **ambivalent** about the importance of cleanliness, the Romans used their engineering skill to meet their sanitation needs.

1. The main purpose of paragraph 1 (lines 1–7) is to
   a. introduce the topic of the passage in a lively manner
   b. question why technological advances are often slow to develop
   c. question the competence of ancient engineers
   d. use an interesting anecdote to get the reader's attention
   e. create suspense

2. Kudos (line 5) most nearly means
   a. accolades
   b. boos
   c. thanks
   d. jobs
   e. profits

3. Infrastructure (line 9) is best defined as
   a. superstructure
   b. foundation
   c. commerce
   d. schools
   e. government

4. According to the writer, who found evidence for an ancient sewage system in the Orkney Islands?
   a. engineers
   b. anthropologists
   c. paleontologists
   d. archaeologists
   e. geologists

5. Which of the following is a reasonable inference from details given in the passage?
   a. Engineers in the Indus Valley were less imaginative than those in the Orkney Islands.
   b. The ancient Romans applied their engineering skills to the problem of sewage disposal more successfully than the ancient Athenians did.
   c. The Emperor Augustus possessed comparatively little foresight.

   d. Networks of brick drains were unnecessary in ancient Athens.
   e. The ancient Romans were indifferent to the importance of good hygiene.

6. Heyday (line 36) most nearly means
   a. declining years
   b. era
   c. golden age
   d. beginning
   e. middle

7. Which of the following best describes the organizational structure of the passage as a whole?
   a. spatial order
   b. order of importance
   c. comparison and contrast
   d. cause and effect
   e. chronological order

8. What was the *Cloaca Maxima* in ancient Rome?
   a. the largest public square in the city
   b. the large brick sewage tunnel that passed through the city center
   c. the leading guild of engineers
   d. the largest aqueduct leading to the city
   e. a broad Roman road

9. Ambivalent (line 51) is best defined as
   a. serious
   b. equivocal
   c. meticulous
   d. clear-cut
   e. compulsive

10. Which of the following best describes the author's tone in the passage?
   a. incensed
   b. objective
   c. melancholy
   d. spirited
   e. resigned

Grammar in Context

In the sentence "<u>One of the earliest attempts at a sewage system</u> that improved upon the impractical practice of hauling away waste and dumping it elsewhere took place about 5,000 years ago in the Orkney Islands, off the coast of Scotland (lines 11–17 on page 105), the independent clause (underlined) expresses the main idea. However, if the author had written " When one of the earliest attempts at a sewage system <u>took place about 5,000 years ago in the Orkney Islands off the coast of Scotland</u>, people improved upon the impractical practice of hauling away waste and dumping it elsewhere," the independent clause would have misleadingly stressed a subordinate idea, rather than the main idea. This error is known as **faulty subordination**.

To avoid faulty subordination, review your sentences for logical emphasis and balance of ideas. For example, make sure that your sentences reflect the relative importance of ideas. Do not use a coordinating conjunction to join ideas of unequal importance. Be careful to link ideas clearly and accurately. Be sure to express cause and effect logically.

On the lines provided, rewrite each of the following sentences to correct faulty subordination. Write "correct" if the sentence is correct.

1. A sewage system must be effective, and it is a key feature in the infrastructure of cities of all sizes.

_____

_____

2. Ancient engineers worked hard on the problem of waste disposal, for they deserve our praise.

_____

_____

3. Stone-lined drains foreshadowed future sewers, and they were built in the Orkney Islands about 5,000 years ago.

_____

_____

4. In the cities of the Indus valley, engineers dealt with the same challenge, and they worked on a grander scale.

_____

_____

5. Surprisingly, waste disposal in ancient Athens was quite unsophisticated.

_____

_____

6. Augustus ruled ancient Rome, and he enclosed an enormous brick sewage tunnel, and it passed right through the city.

_____

_____

Word Associations

In each of the following groups, circle the word that is best defined or suggested by the given phrase.

1. You'll be the death of me yet!
a. protégé   b. nemesis   c. sycophant   d. harbinger

2. how you might characterize the First World War
a. savoir-faire   b. infrastructure   c. cataclysm   d. carte blanche

3. Don't try to sweet talk me!
a. lampoon   b. bode   c. beleaguer   d. inveigle

4. something you shouldn't make a federal case of
a. debauch   b. éclat   c. syndrome   d. peccadillo

5. a behemoth of a man
a. gargantuan   b. philistine   c. malleable   d. prolix

6. The long-winded and repetitive speech bored the entire audience.
a. prototype   b. lampoon   c. tautology   d. bane

7. The sight turned my stomach!
a. picaresque   b. malcontent   c. queasy   d. inchoate

8. They hired all their relatives!
a. nepotism   b. tautology   c. hedonism   d. savoir-faire

9. It just makes me see red!
a. debauch   b. tautology   c. kudos   d. bête noire

10. a crocus in early March
a. bathos   b. philistine   c. harbinger   d. casuistry

11. Long-lasting fatigue is one symptom of the Epstein-Barr virus.
a. tautology   b. syndrome   c. nepotism   d. sycophant

12. The highly touted Broadway play was less than exciting.
a. prolix   b. lackluster   c. dank   d. mellifluous

Choosing the Right Meaning

Read each sentence carefully. Then circle the item that best completes the statement below the sentence.

Because the accused was a protégé and therefore could not be tried, Federal prosecutors arranged to have him deported to his native land, there to be charged   (2)
by his own government.

1. The word **protégé** in line 1 is used to mean
a. trainee
b. someone enjoying
   the patronage of a
   powerful person
c. disciple
d. someone under
   the protection
   of another government

"Given the ghoulish zeal with which the director inflicts these scenes of mayhem and carnage on the audience," observed the critic, "this is most definitely *not* a movie recommended for the fastidious." (2)

2. In line 3 the word **fastidious** most nearly means

a. meticulous   b. finicky   c. easily disgusted   d. overly demanding

Medical authorities grew alarmed when the strange ailment proved refractory and, fearing an outbreak or even an epidemic, quarantined the stricken patients. (2)

3. The best definition for the word **refractory** in line 1 is

a. untreatable   b. unruly   c. disobedient   d. stubborn

"Our natures do pursue,
Like rats that raven down their proper bane,
A thirsty evil; and when we drink, we die." (2)
(Shakespeare, *Measure for Measure*, I, ii, 120–122)

4. The word **bane** in line 2 is used to mean

a. ruin   b. poison   c. death   d. destruction

Antonyms

*In each of the following groups, circle the word or expression that is most nearly the **opposite** of the word in **boldface** type.*

1. gambol
a. wager
b. trace
c. condemn
d. trudge

2. ecumenical
a. lofty
b. evasive
c. parochial
d. amateur

3. ad hoc
a. temporary
b. permanent
c. laughable
d. helpless

4. savoir-faire
a. injustice
b. tactlessness
c. profitability
d. renown

5. de facto
a. by right
b. long-standing
c. sweet tempered
d. clear-cut

6. gargantuan
a. tiny
b. summery
c. soft
d. flighty

7. malcontent
a. unruly
b. disgruntled
c. satisfied
d. fugitive

8. inchoate
a. naked
b. developed
c. conforming
d. immature

9. fastidious
a. squeamish
b. cautious
c. slovenly
d. partial

10. éclat
a. abomination
b. curiosity
c. dullness
d. rarity

11. beatitude
a. cudgel
b. ugliness
c. tension
d. despair

12. lackluster
a. distorted
b. dazzling
c. crass
d. beneficial

13. prolix
a. distant
b. verbose
c. succinct
d. tyrannical

14. imbue
a. expunge
b. lend
c. infuse
d. cancel

15. philistine
a. puny
b. foreign
c. refined
d. boorish

16. dank
a. deserted
b. arid
c. impulsive
d. soaked

Completing the Sentence

From the following list of words, choose the one that best completes each of the following sentences. Write the word in the space provided.

aberration	de facto	imbue	philistine
cataclysm	heyday	malcontent	remand

1. That one unfortunate reaction should be viewed as a(n) _____ rather than as an example of his customary behavior.

2. In order to avoid any further violence, the neighboring states quickly recognized the _____ government established by the military leaders.

3. In their _____ transatlantic passenger ships offered luxury unequaled on the seven seas.

4. Through examples rather than with words, the scoutmaster managed to _____ the troop with worthy ideas and aspirations.

5. I feel sorry for the _____ who always harp on the negative rather than the positive aspects of any situation.

Word Families

A. *On the line provided, write the word you have learned in Units 7–9 that is related to each of the following nouns.*

EXAMPLE: cantankerousness—**cantankerous**

1. ecumenics _____

2. ambivalence _____

3. fastidiousness _____

4. malleability, malleableness _____

5. queasiness _____

6. refractoriness _____

7. prolixity _____

8. inveiglement, inveigler _____

9. fetidness _____

10. dankness _____

11. lampooner, lampoonery _____

12. philistia, philistinism _____

13. aberrant _____

14. debauchee, debauchery _____

15. hedonist _____

16. casuist _____

B. *On the line provided, write the word you have learned in Units 7–9 that is related to each of the following verbs.*

EXAMPLE: depredate—**depredation**

17. empathize _____

18. content _____

19. beatify _____

20. optimize _____

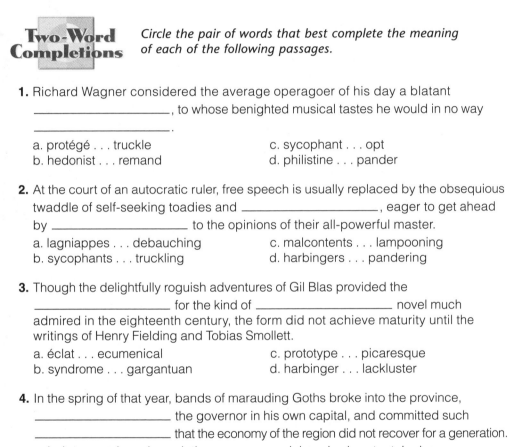

Two-Word Completions — *Circle the pair of words that best complete the meaning of each of the following passages.*

1. Richard Wagner considered the average operagoer of his day a blatant _____, to whose benighted musical tastes he would in no way _____.

a. protégé . . . truckle
b. hedonist . . . remand
c. sycophant . . . opt
d. philistine . . . pander

2. At the court of an autocratic ruler, free speech is usually replaced by the obsequious twaddle of self-seeking toadies and _____, eager to get ahead by _____ to the opinions of their all-powerful master.

a. lagniappes . . . debauching
b. sycophants . . . truckling
c. malcontents . . . lampooning
d. harbingers . . . pandering

3. Though the delightfully roguish adventures of Gil Blas provided the _____ for the kind of _____ novel much admired in the eighteenth century, the form did not achieve maturity until the writings of Henry Fielding and Tobias Smollett.

a. éclat . . . ecumenical
b. syndrome . . . gargantuan
c. prototype . . . picaresque
d. harbinger . . . lackluster

4. In the spring of that year, bands of marauding Goths broke into the province, _____ the governor in his own capital, and committed such _____ that the economy of the region did not recover for a generation.

a. beleaguered . . . depredations
b. lampooned . . . peccadillos
c. debauched . . . tautologies
d. remanded . . . prototypes

mal—bad, ill

This root appears in **malcontent** (page 92), which means "one who is dissatisfied with conditions." Some other words based on the same root are listed below.

maladapted	malfeasance	malfunction	malingerer
malaise	malformation	malice	malodorous

From the list of words above, choose the one that corresponds to each of the brief definitions below. Write the word in the blank space in the illustrative sentence below the definition.

1. unsuited or poorly suited for a particular purpose or situation

The storage area was large enough, but it was _____ for use as a classroom.

2. wrongdoing or misconduct in public office

The politician was accused of _____ when the crooked scheme became public knowledge.

3. one who pretends to be ill in order to escape duty or work

He was fired from the squad because he proved to be a shiftless _____.

4. an abnormal or faulty bodily structure or part

The ravages of disease caused an unsightly _____ of the patient's face.

5. having a bad odor; ill-smelling; highly improper

To my sensibilities, all blue-veined cheeses are unbearably _____.

6. a failure to operate correctly or in a normal manner; to operate poorly or imperfectly

Radio contact was lost for over an hour because of a technical

_____.

7. a desire to cause harm or suffering; deep-seated ill will

Legally, murder is distinguished from manslaughter by the element of _____ aforethought.

8. a vague feeling of physical or mental discomfort

For no evident reason, she was too beset by _____ to attend class.

From the list of words above, choose the one that best completes each of the following sentences. Write the word in the blank space provided.

1. The _____ of a simple switching device set off a chain reaction that culminated in a complete power failure.

2. The woman's delicate constitution and refined sensibility were _____ to the rough-and-tumble life of the frontier.

3. The review panel found the department head guilty of _____ in handling the funds for public housing.

4. Who has not suffered that indefinable sense of _____ that so often accompanies the onset of the flu?

5. A _____ vapor seemed to waft from the fetid bog.

6. Advances in reconstructive surgery now permit doctors to correct many _____ that once were untreatable.

7. Lincoln believed that national unity could never be restored if the South were treated with _____ rather than magnanimity.

8. The new captain personally visited the ship's sickbay to make sure that no _____ were being harbored there.

---

*Circle the **boldface** word that more satisfactorily completes each of the following sentences.*

1. The convertible two-seater sports car is (**maladapted, malodorous**) to the rugged, steep, and icy back roads of the Canadian Rockies.

2. Sociologists posit that the (**malice, malaise**) that makes some Americans feel depressed might lift if those people would become more involved in community activities.

3. A (**malingerer, malfunction**) in the fresh-air circulation system of the office building led the health inspector to evacuate all interior offices that lack windows.

4. Because of an unusual (**malfeasance, malformation**) of the retina in my left eye, my vision cannot be adequately corrected by glasses or by contact lenses.

5. When it is roasted, the edible but (**malodorous, maladapted**) seed of the female ginkgo tree is considered a seasonal delicacy in Japan and China.

6. A (**malingerer, malfunction**) in a closely knit group may escape criticism at first but will one day be exposed and reviled as the weak link in an otherwise effective team.

7. Bees do not sting out of (**malaise, malice**) toward their victims; rather, they sting to survive.

8. The tenacious work of two investigative reporters led to dramatic revelations about the treasurer's (**malformation, malfeasance**) with the company's finances.

Analogies

In each of the following, circle the item that best completes the comparison.

1. bilious is to **queasy** as
a. quizzical is to content
b. contumelious is to elated
c. portentous is to alarmed
d. ambivalent is to sleepy

2. midget is to **minuscule** as
a. fait accompli is to abortive
b. dictum is to risible
c. volte-face is to waggish
d. colossus is to gargantuan

3. tautology is to **redundant** as
a. lampoon is to prolix
b. vignette is to noisome
c. homily is to incoherent
d. solecism is to erroneous

4. prude is to **fastidious** as
a. philistine is to crass
b. prodigy is to lackluster
c. incubus is to prurient
d. hedonist is to malcontent

5. bathos is to **maudlin** as
a. obloquy is to complimentary
b. empathy is to callous
c. persiflage is to picaresque
d. casuistry is to specious

6. inchoate is to **form** as
a. ineffable is to size
b. chimerical is to substance
c. ecumenical is to scope
d. sacrosanct is to duration

7. inveigle is to **flattery** as
a. cozen is to encouragement
b. browbeat is to intimidation
c. reassure is to censure
d. cajole is to criticism

8. mule is to **refractory** as
a. pig is to indolent
b. horse is to iconoclastic
c. fox is to maladroit
d. elephant is to oblivious

9. virtuoso is to **éclat** as
a. gallant is to panache
b. proselyte is to insouciance
c. harbinger is to verisimilitude
d. klutz is to tact

10. aficionado is to **fervid** as
a. pundit is to apathetic
b. sycophant is to caustic
c. connoisseur is to discriminating
d. pessimist is to sanguine

Choosing the Right Meaning

Read each sentence carefully. Then circle the item that best completes the statement below the sentence.

Besides inventing the lens that bears his name, French physicist Augustin-Jean Fresnel (1788–1827) investigated the laws governing the interference of polarized light. (2)

1. The word **polarized** in line 3 is used to mean
a. physically alienated
b. vibrating in a pattern
c. evenly split
d. completely estranged

The summer saw hundreds of volunteers in towns along the rain-swollen Mississippi work around-the-clock, shoring up river levees with sandbags in a desperate effort to hold back the cataclysm. (2)

2. In line 3 the word **cataclysm** most nearly means
a. deluge
b. upheaval
c. catastrophe
d. disaster

"He had often noticed that six months' oblivion amounts to newspaper death, and that resurrection is rare. Nothing is easier, if a man wants it, than rest, profound as the grave." (Henry Adams, *The Education of Henry Adams*)   (2)

3. In line 1 the word **oblivion** is used to mean

a. forgetfulness   b. unawareness   c. being forgotten   d. insensibility

Beleaguered by American and French forces, Lord Cornwallis surrendered his encircled army to George Washington at Yorktown in October 1781.   (2)

4. The best definition for the word **Beleaguered** in line 1 is

a. Outnumbered   b. Troubled   c. Defeated   d. Surrounded

When joke after joke met with dead silence, the comedian began seriously to doubt whether the audience was at all risible.   (2)

5. The word **risible** in line 2 most nearly means

a. laughable   b. ludicrous   c. droll   d. inclined to laugh

Two-Word Completions

Circle the pair of words that best complete the meaning of each of the following sentences.

1. Because her work flouted the canons of classical ballet, Isadora Duncan soon came to be regarded as an artistic _____ to whom nothing was _____.

a. poltroon . . . ambivalent
b. aficionado . . . internecine
c. persona . . . cognate
d. iconoclast . . . sacrosanct

2. Though King Edward VII is often pictured as an effete _____, with appetites as _____ as his physique, he was an intelligent, perceptive observer of the European scene.

a. hedonist . . . gargantuan
b. harbinger . . . fetid
c. pundit . . . philistine
d. mountebank . . . dank

3. "You may consider me a narrow-minded prude," I replied, "but I can see no redeeming social or artistic value in this book. Indeed, it appears to _____ exclusively to the _____ interests of the reader."

a. inveigle . . . bibulous
b. condescend . . . eleemosynary
c. pander . . . prurient
d. opt . . . philistine

4. Boss Tweed and his Tammany Hall cronies were as _____ as hungry sharks; their _____ on New York's treasury left the city in severe financial straits.

a. supine . . . aberrations
b. rapacious . . . depredations
c. effete . . . peccadilloes
d. maladroit . . . lucubrations

5. Though he is somewhat awkward and _____, he handled that ticklish social problem with all the _____ of a born diplomat.

a. lackluster . . . folderol
b. queasy . . . gamut
c. mellifluous . . . prescience
d. maladroit . . . savoir-faire

Enriching Your Vocabulary

Read the passage below. Then complete the exercise at the bottom of the page.

Borrowed Words

"The traitor calmly sipped coffee on the veranda." The preceding sentence, which most English-speakers can readily comprehend, includes words borrowed from French (*traiteur*), Latin (*calma*), Arabic (*qahwa*), and Hindi (*varanda*). One of the beauties of English is its flexibility to incorporate words from many sources. Most people know the powerful influence that Greek and Latin have had on English. But English has also made use of words from many other parts of the world.

As *borrowed* (or *guest*) *words* enter English from other languages, they often undergo modification, especially when their original language has a different alphabet. In some cases, spelling oddities, such as the *b* in *debt* (from Latin, *debitum*), signal the remnants of a word's origin. A borrowed word in Unit 4 is *pundit*, from the Hindi *pandit*. World War II soldiers brought home the Chinese term *gung ho,* which means

"enthusiastically dedicated." Russian has lent us the word *mammoth* (from *mamot*), which means "huge." Turkish has given us the term *yogurt* (from *yoghurt*). Farsi—the language of Iran—has donated the word *shawl* (*shal*). Bantu, an African language, is the source of the noun *banjo* (from *mbanza*). Arawak, a Caribbean tongue, shares with us *iguana* (from *iwana*); and Wolof, a language of Senegal, contributes *banana.*

The common green iguana is found from Mexico southward to Brazil.

In Column A below are 8 more words borrowed from various languages. With or without a dictionary, match each word with its meaning in Column B.

Column A

_____ **1.** amok (amuck)
_____ **2.** boomerang
_____ **3.** caucus
_____ **4.** kowtow
_____ **5.** mufti
_____ **6.** mumbo jumbo
_____ **7.** taboo
_____ **8.** tycoon

Column B

a. unintelligible or incomprehensible language; complicated and seemingly purposeless activity (from Mandingo)

b. to express respect, submission; to show servile deference (from Chinese)

c. a prohibition excluding something from use or mention; forbidden (from Tongan)

d. a flat, curved stick that returns when thrown (from Dharuk)

e. a powerful, highly successful business person (from Japanese)

f. a closed meeting of members of a political party (from Algonquian)

g. civilian dress, especially when worn by someone who usually wears a uniform (from Arabic)

h. in a frenzy of violence; in a blind, undisciplined manner (from Malay)

Definitions

Note carefully the spelling, pronunciation, part(s) of speech, and definition(s) of each of the following words. Then write the word in the blank space(s) in the illustrative sentence(s) following. Finally, study the lists of synonyms and antonyms given at the end of each entry.

1. acumen
(a kyü' mən)

(*n.*) keenness of insight; quickness or accuracy of judgment

Stars who enjoy long careers generally choose their roles with remarkable _____.

SYNONYMS: perspicacity, shrewdness, acuity
ANTONYMS: ignorance, stupidity, obtuseness

2. adjudicate
(ə jüd' i kāt)

(*v.*) to act as judge in a matter; to settle through the use of a judge or legal tribunal

An arbitrator may sometimes _____ a civil suit involving a relatively small sum of money.

SYNONYMS: arbitrate, referee, mediate

3. anachronism
(ə nak' rə niz əm)

(*n.*) a chronological misplacing of events, objects, customs, or persons in regard to each other

To avoid introducing _____ into their work, authors of historical novels must do painstaking research.

SYNONYM: chronological error

4. apocryphal
(ə pok' rə fəl)

(*adj.*) of doubtful or questionable authenticity

Although his tales of youthful derring-do are probably _____, they are very entertaining.

SYNONYMS: fictitious, mythical, spurious, bogus
ANTONYMS: authentic, genuine, true

5. disparity
(dis par' ə tē)

(*n.*) a difference or inequality in age, rank, degree, amount, or quality; a dissimilarity, unlikeness

The growing _____ between the rich and the poor is a matter of grave concern.

SYNONYMS: discrepancy, incongruity
ANTONYMS: similarity, likeness, congruity

6. dissimulate
(di sim' yə lāt)

(*v.*) to hide or disguise one's true thoughts, feelings, or intentions

In awkward social situations, it is sometimes more courteous to _____ than to be straightforward.

SYNONYMS: dissemble, pretend, misrepresent
ANTONYM: reveal

7. empirical
(em pir' i kəl)

(*adj.*) derived from, dependent upon, or guided by practical experience, observation, or experiment, rather than by theory; so verifiable

The compilation of _____ data is an essential part of sound scientific research.

SYNONYMS: observed, experiential, pragmatic
ANTONYMS: theoretical, hypothetical, conjectural

8. flamboyant
(flam boi′ ənt)

(*adj.*) highly elaborate or ornate; vividly colored; strikingly brilliant or bold

We were dazzled by the _____ plumage of the birds in the tropical rain forest.

SYNONYMS: showy, ostentatious, florid
ANTONYMS: staid, sedate, decorous, seemly, sober

9. fulsome
(fŭl′ səm)

(*adj.*) offensively insincere or excessive; disgusting, sickening

It is best to take the _____ praise that appears in movie ads with a grain of salt.

SYNONYMS: inordinate, repulsive
ANTONYMS: understated, muted, restrained, agreeable

10. immolate
(im′ ə lāt)

(*v.*) to kill as a sacrifice, especially by fire; to destroy or renounce for the sake of another

When the Aztecs took captives, they enslaved some and _____ others.

SYNONYMS: slay, kill
ANTONYMS: save, rescue, preserve

11. imperceptible
(im pər sep′ tə bəl)

(*adj.*) extremely slight; incapable of being perceived by the senses or the mind

When two candidates agree on most issues, voters may find the differences between them _____.

SYNONYMS: minimal, undetectable
ANTONYMS: conspicuous, noticeable, flagrant

12. lackey
(lak′ ē)

(*n.*) a uniformed male servant; a servile follower

A wealthy Victorian household generally included numerous maids, _____, and other domestics.

SYNONYMS: footman, toady, flunky, hanger-on
ANTONYMS: lord, liege, employer, boss

13. liaison
(lē′ ə zon)

(*n.*) the contact or means of communication between groups; someone acting as such a contact; any close relationship; a thickening or binding agent used in cooking

Block associations serve as _____ between neighborhoods and city governments.

SYNONYMS: intermediary, channel

14. monolithic
(mon ə lith′ ik)

(*adj.*) characterized by massiveness, solidness, and total uniformity

The government buildings in the state's capital can best
be described as _____ in style.
SYNONYMS: undifferentiated, massive, dense
ANTONYMS: diversified, variform, multifarious

15. mot juste
(mō zhüst′)

(*n.*) the most suitable or exact word or expression
The erudite film and theater critic always managed to find
the _____ to sum up her opinion.
SYNONYM: right word
ANTONYMS: misnomer, misusage, malapropism

16. nihilism
(nī′ əl iz əm)

(*n.*) a total rejection of existing laws, institutions, and moral
values; extreme radicalism
Those who rebel against the restraints imposed by society
may be attracted to _____.
ANTONYM: conservatism

17. patrician
(pə trish′ ən)

(*n.*) a member of the ruling class; a person of high or noble
rank or of prominent social standing; (*adj.*) belonging to,
befitting, or characteristic of such a person
Though her origins were humble, she had the assurance
and bearing of a _____.
Many scions of _____ families
feel obliged to choose a life of public service.
SYNONYMS: (*n.*) aristocrat, peer, noble; (*adj.*) highborn
ANTONYMS: (*n.*) peasant, commoner, plebeian

18. propitiate
(prō pish′ ē āt)

(*v.*) to make someone or something favorably inclined toward
oneself; to conciliate, satisfy, or appease
Many ancient peoples practiced rituals involving offerings
and sacrifices to _____ their gods.
SYNONYMS: placate, mollify
ANTONYMS: estrange, alienate, provoke, annoy

19. sic
(sik)

(*adv.*) thus so; intentionally written so
The American poet e.e. cummings [_____]
paid close attention to the way his poems looked when
set in type.

20. sublimate
(səb′ lə māt)

(*v.*) to redirect the energy of a biological or instinctual impulse
into a higher or more acceptable channel
If we are to live in harmony with one another, we must learn to
_____ our aggressive impulses.
SYNONYMS: rechannel, elevate

Completing the Sentence

From the words for this unit, choose the one that best completes each of the following sentences. Write the word in the space provided.

1. The company's profits increased remarkably last year, thanks mainly to the new president's exceptional business _____.

2. Although these stories have been widely accepted for many years, we now have ample evidence to show that they are completely _____.

3. Then she leaned toward me and said confidingly, "Between you and I [_____], I didn't believe a word he said."

4. As the duke's coach drew up, two _____ in splendid livery stepped forth to open the carriage door.

5. The fate of individuals accused of war crimes may be _____ by an international court.

6. The able auctioneer acknowledged bids from the audience that were so discreet as to be _____ to the untrained eye.

7. What a shock it was for her to discover the unworthiness of the cause for which she had _____ her youth, her talents, and her hopes of happiness.

8. We need not try actively to _____ the opponents of our candidate, but we can certainly take reasonable precautions to avoid antagonizing them.

9. During the campaign in West Virginia in 1861, Robert E. Lee acted as the _____ between the commanders of the two independent Confederate brigades operating in the area.

10. Though I believed their promises at first, I soon came to realize the great _____ between their words and their deeds.

11. It is one thing to spin out ingenious theories; it is quite another to find _____ confirmation for them.

12. I know you're trying to curry favor with the boss, but must you greet each and every one of his bright ideas with such _____ flattery?

13. In calling them "stinkers," I may not have been too refined; but in view of their disgraceful conduct, I think I applied the _____.

14. The aggressive drive can be channeled into antisocial forms of behavior or _____ into loftier, more worthwhile endeavors.

15. A major political party in the United States represents a coalition of many different views and interests, rather than a(n) _____ structure.

16. His efforts to _____ his feelings of inadequacy by pretending to be bored and indifferent are a sign of immaturity.

17. Having the Civil War general sign documents with a ballpoint pen struck me as the most ludicrous _____ in the whole miniseries.

10

18. During the early years of the Roman Republic, plebeians vied bitterly with _____ for political dominance.

19. Their blanket rejection of the standards and values on which our society is founded seems to be little short of senseless _____.

20. One would expect such _____ behavior from an attention-seeking celebrity, not from a normally shy, unassuming person.

Synonyms

*Choose the word from this unit that is **the same** or **most nearly the same** in meaning as the **boldface** word or expression in the given phrase. Write the word on the line provided.*

1. letters that proved to be **spurious** _____

2. based on **experiential** evidence _____

3. surrounded by **flunkies** _____

4. sustained **minimal** damage _____

5. learned to **rechannel** their impulses _____

6. known for wearing **showy** outfits _____

7. has a tendency to **dissemble** _____

8. sought to **placate** their supervisor _____

9. embarrassed by the **inordinate** thanks _____

10. a group of **undifferentiated** structures _____

11. called to **mediate** the dispute _____

12. an **intermediary** we can rely on _____

13. said it was a pitty [**thus so**] _____

14. sought the **right word** with which to end the speech _____

15. filled with **chronological errors** _____

Antonyms

*Choose the word from this unit that is **most nearly opposite** in meaning to the **boldface** word or expression in the given phrase. Write the word on the line provided.*

16. descended from **peasants** _____

17. acted with surprising **ignorance** _____

18. a group that espouses **conservatism** _____

19. a plan to **rescue** the hostages _____

20. the **similarities** between their stories _____

Unit 10 ■ 121

 **Choosing the Right Word**

*Circle the **boldface** word that more satisfactorily completes each of the following sentences.*

1. The main character in the comedy is a bumbling inventor who has accidentally transported himself into the past, there to suffer the misadventures of a hapless (**lackey, anachronism**).

2. When you say that your rival has a talent for (**disparity, dissimulation**), what you really mean is that he is an out-and-out phony.

3. The story about Bunker Hill and "Don't fire until you see the whites of their eyes" may be (**monolithic, apocryphal**), but I like it, and I'm going to continue believing it.

4. While I agree that there are imperfections in our society, I simple cannot accept your (**imperceptible, nihilistic**) belief that the entire heritage of the past must be discarded.

5. There seemed no point in the author's gratuitous use of such (**fulsome, apocryphal**) language other than to offend the taste of the reader.

6. She is so concerned with words that she seems to think the only thing that is needed to deal with a problem is to find the (**mot juste, anachronism**) to describe it.

7. There is probably nothing worse than having (**patrician, apocryphal**) tastes on an income better suited to the lifestyle of a pauper.

8. People who engage in self-destructive behavior seem to have a desire to (**propitiate, immolate**) themselves.

9. There is often a (**liaison, disparity**) between what people aspire to do and what they are equipped to do by natural endowment and training.

10. It's no wonder he's got such a swelled head when all those (**patricians, lackeys**) that tag along after him do nothing but sing his praises.

11. Those solemn religious ceremonies are intended to protect the tribe from disasters by (**propitiating, adjudicating**) the gods who control natural phenomena.

12. Some psychologists theorize that genius in any field represents a special kind of (**immolation, sublimation**) of capacities, drives, and needs that are in all of us.

13. American voters may be amused by a (**patrician, flamboyant**) personality, but they seem to prefer more sober types when making their choice for high public office.

14. Because deadly carbon monoxide gas can be neither seen nor smelled, its presence is practically (**empirical, imperceptible**).

15. In a campaign speech the candidate said, "My opponent has flaunted ([**sic**], **mot juste**) all of the principles of sound fiscal management."

16. We are not suggesting that students should run the school, but we believe that the administration should maintain a (**nihilism, liaison**) with the students.

17. No country can survive the combined threat of foreign invasion and domestic insurrection unless it is governed by leaders possessing extraordinary political (**acumen, disparity**).

18. Though Plato's approach to philosophy often seems somewhat mystical, Aristotle's is decidedly (**empirical, fulsome**).

19. In a pluralistic democracy, such as the United States, there is little chance that a (**flamboyant, monolithic**) public opinion will ever develop on any controversial issue.

20. When a small sum is involved, the cost of (**adjudication, dissimulation**) can exceed the amount of the award.

*Read the following passage, in which some of the words you have studied in this unit appear in **boldface** type. Then complete each statement given below the passage by circling the letter of the item that is **the same** or **almost the same** in meaning as the highlighted word.*

Who Got Here First?

(Line)

Who were the first Americans? Where did they come from, and how and when did they get here? For a long time, the archaeological community accepted a seemingly **monolithic** body of **empirical** evidence supporting the theory that the earliest Americans were Siberian hunters who crossed the dry
(5) land bridge at the Bering Strait at the close of the last ice age, around 11,500 years ago. This conclusion was based on unique stone projectile points found near Clovis, New Mexico, which date from that time.

Pre-Clovis wooden digging stick, about 12,230 years old, found at Monte Verde

Now, however, a growing body of evidence
(10) presents certain **disparities** that cast doubt upon this theory. Recent discoveries indicate that the first Americans may have arrived much earlier, by different routes, and from different parts of the world.

(15) Primarily responsible for the change in thinking are two intriguing finds: a pre-Clovis camp in Monte Verde, Chile, and a male skeleton found in Washington State that bears little resemblance to the skeletons of Siberian
(20) origin. These discoveries, and those of pre-Clovis artifacts found in several eastern states, have given rise to new theories.

One theory attempts to explain the early dates of the Chilean site by suggesting that people
(25) migrated down the Pacific coast in skin-covered boats. Another tries to explain the early dates of the East Coast sites by suggesting that early Europeans sailed close to the coasts of Greenland and Iceland to cross the North Atlantic. A third theory proposes that people from Southeast Asia went to Australia first and then crossed the Pacific to South America.

(30) Some of these new theories may eventually prove to be **apocryphal**. But the ongoing debate is lively and sometimes heated. It is an exciting time indeed to be an archaeologist.

---

1. The meaning of **monolithic** (line 3) is
  a. diversified   c. genuine
  b. massive   d. suspicious

2. Empirical (line 3) most nearly means
  a. statistical   c. circumstantial
  b. theoretical   d. observed

3. Disparities (line 10) is best defined as
  a. incongruities   c. similarities
  b. indications   d. details

4. The meaning of **apocryphal** (line 30) is
  a. ridiculous   c. bogus
  b. authentic   d. intriguing

Definitions

Note carefully the spelling, pronunciation, part(s) of speech, and definition(s) of each of the following words. Then write the word in the blank space(s) in the illustrative sentence(s) following. Finally, study the lists of synonyms and antonyms given at the end of each entry.

1. apostate
(ə pos′ tāt)

(*n.*) one who forsakes his or her religion, party, or cause

A politician who switches parties can expect to be denounced by former allies as an _____.

SYNONYMS: renegade, defector, turncoat
ANTONYMS: true believer, loyalist

2. bravado
(brə vä′ dō)

(*n.*) a display of false or assumed courage

The challenger's boast that he would knock the champ out in the first round was sheer _____.

SYNONYMS: swagger, bluster, braggadocio
ANTONYMS: mettle, bravery, pluck

3. consensus
(kən sen′ səs)

(*n.*) a collective or general agreement of opinion, feeling, or thinking

After an unusually contentious debate, the council finally reached a _____.

SYNONYMS: unanimity, concord, accord, harmony
ANTONYMS: dissension, discord, disagreement

4. constrict
(kən strikt′)

(*v.*) to make smaller or narrower, draw together, squeeze; to stop or cause to falter

An accident or road repairs can _____ the flow of traffic on a busy highway.

SYNONYMS: contract, curb, restrain
ANTONYMS: enlarge, dilate, expand

5. dichotomy
(dī kot′ ə mē)

(*n.*) a division into two contradictory or mutually exclusive parts; a branching or forking in an ancestral line

Many of the world's great works of literature examine the _____ between good and evil.

SYNONYMS: schism, division, bifurcation
ANTONYMS: uniformity, oneness

6. effusive
(i fyü′ siv)

(*adj.*) highly demonstrative; unrestrained

I received such an _____ welcome from my hosts that I felt like the party's guest of honor.

SYNONYMS: gushy, lavish
ANTONYMS: restrained, reserved, muted, subdued

7. euphoria
(yü fôr′ ē ə)

(*n.*) a feeling of great happiness or well-being, often with no objective basis

It is perfectly normal for a person who wins the lottery to feel an initial surge of _____ .

SYNONYMS: elation, bliss, ecstasy, rapture
ANTONYMS: melancholy, depression, gloom

8. gothic
(goth′ ik)

(*adj.*) characterized by or emphasizing a gloomy setting and grotesque or violent events; such a literary or artistic style; a type of medieval architecture

In many a _____ novel, the life of the brooding protagonist is blighted by a dark secret.

SYNONYMS: sinister, eerie

9. impasse
(im′ pas)

(*n.*) a dead end; a position from which there is no escape; a problem to which there is no solution

When negotiations reached an _____ , the workers went out on strike.

SYNONYMS: deadlock, standoff, stalemate

10. lugubrious
(lù gü′ brē əs)

(*adj.*) sad, mournful, or gloomy, especially to an exaggerated or ludicrous degree

The clown's _____ face, complete with a painted teardrop, never fails to make the audience laugh.

SYNONYMS: doleful, melancholy, dismal, dolorous
ANTONYMS: merry, jovial, hilarious, funny

11. metamorphosis
(met ə môr′ fə sis)

(*n.*) a complete transformation, as if by magic

The beauty makeovers that we sometimes see on talk shows are a kind of _____ .

SYNONYMS: change, makeover

12. mystique
(mi stēk′)

(*n.*) an aura or attitude of mystery or veneration surrounding something or someone

A _____ still clings to some of the great movie stars of the past.

SYNONYMS: charisma

13. non sequitur
(non sek′ wi tər)

(*n.*) an inference or conclusion that does not follow logically from the facts or premises

When it was the next debater's turn, he confounded us with an argument undermined by _____ .

SYNONYMS: illogical reference, unsound conclusion

14. parlous
(pär′ ləs)

(adj.) full of danger or risk, perilous

In a televised speech, the president warned the nation that it faced _____ times.

SYNONTMS: hazardous, risky, dangerous
ANTONYMS: safe, secure, risk-free

15. punctilio
(pəŋk til′ ē ō)

(n.) a minute detail of conduct or procedure; an instant of time

The mark of a true perfectionist is the need to check each and every _____ personally.

SYNONYMS: fine point, nicety

16. quagmire
(kwag′ mīr)

(n.) soft, soggy mud or slush; a difficult or entrapping situation

After a week of heavy rain, the farmer's fields were reduced to a _____.

SYNONYMS: fen, marsh, bog, morass
ANTONYMS: bedrock, solid footing, terra firma

17. quixotic
(kwik sot′ ik)

(adj.) extravagantly or romantically idealistic; visionary without regard to practical considerations

Utopian fiction presents _____ fantasies of ideal social orders.

SYNONYMS: fanciful, impractical, utopian
ANTONYMS: realistic, down-to-earth, pragmatic

18. raconteur
(rak on tər′)

(n.) a person who tells stories and anecdotes with great skill

The author, a noted _____, was much sought after as a dinner party guest.

SYNONYMS: storyteller, anecdotist

19. sine qua non
(sin ə kwä nōn′)

(n.) an essential or indispensable element or condition

The _____ for a successful paty is a group of interesting and sociable guests.

SYNONYMS: necessity, requisite, desideratum

20. vendetta
(ven det′ ə)

(n.) a prolonged feud, often between two families, characterized by retaliatory acts of revenge; any act motivated by vengeance

The two novelists, once good friends, have been carrying on a literary _____ for more than two decades.

SYNONYMS: blood feud, rivalry

Completing the Sentence

From the words for this unit, choose the one that best completes each of the following sentences. Write the word in the space provided.

1. Every great president must combine various roles—the practical politician, the masterful intellectual, the tough administrator, the persuasive advocate—and at least a touch of the _____ visionary.

2. Although it may be true that hard work does not guarantee success, it is certainly a(n) _____ for doing well in any endeavor.

3. His challenge to fight was pure _____; inwardly he hoped that no one would take him on.

4. It took Rome centuries to achieve the miraculous _____ from a minor city-state on the banks of the Tiber to the leading power in the Mediterranean world.

5. One look at the coach's _____ expression, and I knew that all our misgivings about the outcome of the game had been borne out.

6. Modern military power requires great industrial resources, but to conclude from this that industrialized nations are inherently militaristic is a _____ .

7. To achieve an hourglass figure, fashionable ladies of the nineteenth century employed tight-fitting corsets to _____ their waistlines.

8. Hemingway's *Death in the Afternoon* offers a rare insight into the _____ of the bullring and the attitudes that surround that ancient blood sport.

9. Not until later did I realize that their _____ expressions of interest in our welfare were insincere and self-serving.

10. The police investigation established that the victim was not an innocent bystander but the target of a gangland _____ .

11. When he came to the throne, Julian the _____ renounced Christianity and began a vigorous campaign to reestablish paganism as the official religion of the Roman Empire.

12. You cannot duck your responsibility for negotiating an agreement simply by announcing that you have reached a hopeless _____ .

13. As the disappointing results of the poll filtered in, the candidate sank into a(n) _____ of doubts about the future.

14. Each episode in the silent-movie serial *The Perils of Pauline* ended with the heroine facing another _____ predicament.

15. The mood of _____ brought about by our extraordinary good fortune caused us to relax our usual alertness.

16. Though everyone in our club agreed that we had a problem, there was no group _____ on how to solve it.

17. The rugged landscape, with the severe vertical lines of the mountains in the background, lent an air of _____ gloom to the entire scene.

18. How can you concern yourself with the _____ of protocol when your whole world is collapsing about your ears?

19. The speakers said that they could see little hope for world peace unless something could be done to bridge the _____ between the "have" and the "have-not" nations.

20. The man was a skilled _____ whose repertory of amusing anecdotes was seemingly inexhaustible.

Synonyms

*Choose the word from this unit that is **the same** or **most nearly the same** in meaning as the **boldface** word or expression in the given phrase. Write the word on the line provided.*

1. attend to each **fine point** myself _____

2. **fanciful** plans for solving the problem _____

3. an extremely **risky** undertaking _____

4. unable to break the **deadlock** _____

5. the glaring **division** between wealth and poverty _____

6. waged a **blood feud** for generations _____

7. an **eerie** story of betrayal and madness _____

8. heaped **lavish** praise upon the performance _____

9. a **storyteller** without equal _____

10. was not deceived by my opponent's **bluster** _____

11. stuck in the **bog** _____

12. has a certain **charisma** _____

13. a **requisite** for good health _____

14. underwent a truly remarkable **transformation** _____

15. a series of **unsound conclusions** _____

Antonyms

*Choose the word from this unit that is **most nearly opposite** in meaning to the **boldface** word or expression in the given phrase. Write the word on the line provided.*

16. overcome by **melancholy** when I heard the news _____

17. a meeting that ended in **discord** _____

18. sang a **merry** ballad _____

19. caused the vessels to **dilate** _____

20. has a reputation for being a **loyalist** _____

Choosing the Right Word

*Circle the **boldface** word that more satisfactorily completes each of the following sentences.*

1. Even though their son had abandoned the religion in which he had been brought up, his parents never thought of him as an (**apostate, impasse**).

2. I wanted a direct, factual explanation of what had happened, but all I got was emotional (**effusions, quagmires**) describing in painful detail how much they had suffered.

3. For a long time we lived under the illusion that "everything would come out all right," but inevitably we arrived at the (**vendetta, impasse**) where we had to face realities.

4. Our thesis was that at this stage in their history, Americans must eschew the (**sine qua non, mystique**) of force and violence and develop new ideals of social cooperation.

5. Their analysis of the problem seemed to me extremely fallacious—full of false assumptions, dubious generalizations, and (**constrictions, non sequiturs**).

6. There are times when I like to read a (**gothic, parlous**) tale of gloomy castles, mysterious strangers, and unhappy romances.

7. Space suits are designed to afford astronauts maximum protection without unduly (**constricting, dichotomizing**) their freedom of movement.

8. Perhaps her volunteering to undertake the mission was mere (**bravado, consensus**), but the fact remains that she did accomplish everything that was expected of her.

9. As we learned to understand each other's needs and aspirations, a sort of unspoken (**consensus, impasse**) developed that enabled us to work together harmoniously.

10. It is impossible for me to convey the intensity of emotion that I felt at that (**lugubrious, euphoric**) moment when I learned I had won the scholarship.

11. There is no point in trying to decide exactly which of the factors is most important for victory in the election; every one of them is a (**non sequitur, sine qua non**).

12. The ordeal of the Civil War (**apostasized, metamorphosed**) Lincoln from an obscure small-town lawyer into a historical personality of universal appeal.

13. Does it seem paradoxical that like many other great comedians, she goes about with a characteristically (**lugubrious, quixotic**) expression on her face?

14. Despite the grave risks that the rescue attempt would entail, there was no shortage of volunteers for the (**parlous, effusive**) undertaking.

15. Very few of the world's problems can be understood in terms of a simple (**euphoria, dichotomy**) of right and wrong.

16. The new assistant dean's adherence to every (**mystique, punctilio**) in the Student Code alienated both the faculty and the student body.

17. In *Romeo and Juliet*, the hero's tragic death comes as the result of a long-standing (**vendetta, bravado**) between his family and Juliet's.

18. Though your efforts to enact a program of ecological reform in the face of strong opposition were (**quixotic, gothic**) and doomed to failure, they were inspiring.

19. It's laughable of you to think that you are an accomplished (**raconteur, apostate**) just because you have memorized an assortment of feeble old jokes.

20. Involvement in the long war in Vietnam led the United States into a (**consensus, quagmire**) from which it was extremely difficult to withdraw.

Vocabulary in Context

*Read the following passage, in which some of the words you have studied in this unit appear in **boldface** type. Then complete each statement given below the passage by circling the letter of the item that is **the same** or **almost the same** in meaning as the highlighted word.*

The Erie Canal

(Line)

Skeptics called the idea **quixotic**. Critics called it "Clinton's big ditch." But DeWitt Clinton, the governor of New York, ignored them all. He successfully pushed for building a canal that would connect New York City with the Great Lakes.

Construction began in 1817. Despite predictions that the canal would prove to be a **quagmire**, the project proceeded smoothly. Parts of the Erie Canal were (5) operating as early as 1820. When it was fully completed in 1825, at a cost of $7

million, the canal linked the Hudson River with Buffalo on Lake Erie. The waterway was 40 feet wide, 4 feet (10) deep, and 363 miles long— 335 miles longer than any other canal in the country.

Euphoria greeted the canal's completion. (15) Celebrations took place in New York City and Buffalo. River towns boomed. Goods from the South and West could be shipped (20)

Boats were drawn along the Erie Canal by horses on the towpath.

east faster and cheaper than ever before. And as quickly and inexpensively as the canal brought western goods east, it took immigrants west to the frontier. Only the canal's width and depth **constricted** traffic, but these dimensions were soon increased. The Erie Canal was a huge success, and New York City emerged as the port through which every major trade route passed. (25)

The sharp drop in travel times and in costs quickly got the attention of government officials. The **consensus** was that canal building was in order, and by 1849, 3300 miles of canals crossed the Northeast and Midwest. But a new, faster, and cheaper form of transportation was on the rise: the railroad. The heyday of canals was over. (30)

---

1. The meaning of **quixotic** (line 1) is
a. impractical
b. pragmatic
c. difficult
d. costly

2. Quagmire (line 5) most nearly means
a. bonanza
b. mistake
c. morass
d. bore

3. Euphoria (line 14) is best defined as
a. depression
b. annoyance
c. elation
d. fear

4. The meaning of **constricted** (line 23) is
a. expanded
b. policed
c. slowed
d. restrained

5. Consensus (line 27) most nearly means
a. agreement
b. decision
c. discord
d. proposal

Definitions

Note carefully the spelling, pronunciation, part(s) of speech, and definition(s) of each of the following words. Then write the word in the blank space(s) in the illustrative sentence(s) following. Finally, study the lists of synonyms and antonyms given at the end of each entry.

1. apposite
(ap′ ə zit)

(*adj.*) appropriate; suitable; apt

I did my best to give an _____ answer to each of the interviewer's questions.
SYNONYMS: relevant, pertinent, material, germane
ANTONYMS: irrelevant, immaterial, inappropriate

2. augur
(ô′ ger)

(*n.*) a prophet or seer; (*v.*) to predict, foreshadow

The old man who lived alone in the forest was believed by the villagers to be a(n) _____.

The news did not _____ well for the health of the economy in the short term.
SYNONYMS: (*n.*) oracle; (*v.*) bode

3. bilk
(bilk)

(*v.*) to defraud, cheat, or swindle; to evade payment of; to frustrate, thwart

There will always be people who are only too ready to _____ credulous individuals.
SYNONYMS: dupe, cozen

4. charisma
(kə riz′ mə)

(*n.*) the special personal magnetism that makes an individual exceptionally appealing to other people; a divinely bestowed gift or power

According to leading pundits, the dynamic young politician has the _____ of a born leader.
SYNONYMS: appeal, charm, mystique

5. debilitate
(di bil′ ə tāt)

(*v.*) to make weak or feeble

Illness _____ the patient so severely that she was no longer able to perform even the simplest everyday chores.
SYNONYMS: enervate, sap, exhaust, enfeeble
ANTONYMS: strengthen, fortify, invigorate

6. execrable
(ek′ si krə bəl)

(*adj.*) utterly detestable, hateful, or abhorrent; extremely inferior

The crude and _____ behavior of a few individuals spoiled the evening for the rest of us.
SYNONYMS: odious, abominable, reprehensible
ANTONYMS: commendable, praiseworthy, meritorious

7. impinge
(im pinj')

(*v.*) to strike against or collide with violently; to encroach or obtrude upon; to make an impression upon

Political forces sometimes _____ on our everyday lives.

SYNONYMS: horn in, affect

8. labyrinth
(lab' ə rinth)

(*n.*) a bewildering maze; any confusing or complicated situation

I quickly lost my way as I wandered through the old city's _____ of winding streets.

SYNONYMS: tangle, mystery, enigma

9. narcissism
(när' sə siz əm)

(*n.*) excessive self-love; absorption in oneself

Because of her _____, she was completely unwilling to listen to other people's opinions.

SYNONYMS: egotism, conceit, vanity, amour propre

10. niggardly
(nig' ərd lē)

(*adj.*) stingy; meanly small or insufficient

The old miser was as _____ with his advice as he was with his money.

SYNONYMS: tightfisted, penny-pinching, mean
ANTONYMS: generous, bountiful, magnanimous

11. pastiche
(pas tēsh')

(*n.*) a dramatic, musical, or literary work made up of bits and pieces from other sources; a hodgepodge

The figure skater performed to a _____ of melodies from *Carmen*.

SYNONYMS: medley, patchwork, melange, potpourri

12. precarious
(pri kâr' ē əs)

(*adj.*) very uncertain or unsure; dangerous or risky

A long period of unemployment left my friend in a financially _____ position.

SYNONYMS: perilous, dubious, ticklish
ANTONYMS: secure, safe, sturdy, firm

13. rapport
(ra pôr')

(*n.*) a close and harmonious relationship

The players in a chamber music ensemble need to develop an excellent _____.

SYNONYMS: bond, tie, affinity, understanding

14. utilitarian
(yü til ə târ' ē ən)

(*adj.*) stressing practicality over other considerations; relating to the belief that what is good or desirable is determined purely by its usefulness

The layout and organization of the busy restaurant's small kitchen were strictly _____.

SYNONYMS: practical, functional, pragmatic
ANTONYMS: nonfunctional, ornamental, decorative

15. vacuous
(vak′ yü əs)

(*adj.*) devoid of matter, substance, or meaning; lacking ideas or intelligence; purposeless

From the _____ expression on your face, no one would guess that you have such a sharp mind.

SYNONYMS: inane, insipid, fatuous, void, empty
ANTONYMS: incisive, trenchant, perceptive, intelligent

16. vagary
(vā′ gə rē)

(*n.*) an unpredictable, erratic, or seemingly purposeless action, occurrence, or notion

Who can explain the _____ of the world of high fashion?

SYNONYMS: caprice, whim, quirk

17. viable
(vī′ ə bəl)

(*adj.*) capable of living or developing under normal circumstances

The mayor announced a _____ plan to reduce traffic in the downtown business district.

SYNONYMS: practicable, workable, feasible
ANTONYMS: impracticable, unworkable, unfeasible

18. xenophobia
(zen ə fō′ bē ə)

(*n.*) undue or unreasonable fear, hatred, or contempt of foreigners or strangers or of what is foreign or strange

It is sad when people who themselves were once newcomers to a land are blinded by _____.

SYNONYMS: provinciality, parochialism, chauvinism

19. zany
(zā′ nē)

(*adj.*) clownish or funny in a crazy, bizarre, or ludicrous way; (*n.*) one who plays the clown

Who doesn't love the _____ antics of the Marx brothers?

In every sitcom, there is a goofy character who can best be described as a _____.

SYNONYMS: (*adj.*) comical, daffy; (*n.*) buffoon
ANTONYMS: (*adj.*) sedate, decorous, prim, sober, grave

20. zealot
(zel′ ət)

(*n.*) a fanatical partisan; an ardent follower

When it comes to our school's hockey team, my brother can best be described as a _____.

SYNONYMS: fanatic, extremist

Completing the Sentence

From the words for this unit, choose the one that best completes each of the following sentences. Write the word in the space provided.

1. Only after living and working in Washington for many years were we able to find our way through the vast _____ of government departments and agencies.

2. When we asked the climbers why they wanted to scale the mountain, they gave the _____ reply, "Because it's there."

3. His _____ remarks revealed how little he really knew about political economy.

4. Since the play is essentially a(n) _____ of devices and ideas drawn from many different sources, it lacks the consistency and cohesiveness of the writer's other works.

5. "Any organization that is able to survive and prosper in these trying times has indeed proven itself _____," she observed.

6. Instead of sentimentalizing about the passing of rural America, we must work to achieve an effective _____ with our modern urban environment.

7. Luxury and self-indulgence _____ the once vigorous Roman people and led to the fall of the empire.

8. Some leaders have such great personal _____ that they inspire an attitude akin to religious veneration in their followers.

9. Our party can use the support of ardent young _____, but we also need the help of older and cooler heads.

10. We recognize the need for vigorous criticism in a political campaign, but we will certainly not tolerate that kind of _____ character assassination.

11. Attacked from all sides by superior forces, the army found itself in a(n) _____, if not totally untenable, position.

12. Although I am not one of the more prosperous members of the community, my contributions to charity are by no means _____.

13. We cannot say with any confidence how long this trip will take us because our progress is dependent upon the _____ of the weather.

14. Oscar Wilde's famous epigram that "Self-love is the beginning of a life-long romance" is a clever comment on _____.

15. Only later did we come to realize that there was a serious purpose behind his apparently frivolous remarks and _____ behavior.

16. I cannot accept a purely _____ view of life that ignores such aspects of human experience as beauty, love, and humor.

17. By filing false claims over a period of many years, the pair attempted to _____ the insurance company of large sums of money.

18. As I lay there, drifting off to sleep, suddenly the sound of a very loud, very raucous, and very obnoxious television commercial _____ on my ears.

19. The fumble by our quarterback on the opening kickoff, followed by a 15-yard penalty against us, did not _____ well for our team.

20. Their consistent attitude of hostility toward any cultural tradition different from their own cannot be excused by calling it _____.

Synonyms

*Choose the word from this unit that is **the same** or **most nearly the same** in meaning as the **boldface** word or expression in the given phrase. Write the word on the line provided.*

1. a **patchwork** of other people's ideas   _____

2. results that **bode** well for our success   _____

3. **duped** the unsuspecting couple   _____

4. subject to the **whims** of fortune   _____

5. has a reputation as a **fanatic**   _____

6. could never be accused of **egotism**   _____

7. a disease that **enfeebles** those who contract it   _____

8. **relevant** to the matter being discussed   _____

9. **obtrudes** on the rights of others   _____

10. denounced their **odious** behavior   _____

11. a **tangle** of rules and regulations   _____

12. friends who have a unique **bond**   _____

13. possesses undeniable **charm**   _____

14. a strictly **functional** design   _____

15. criticized the politician's **chauvinism**   _____

Antonyms

*Choose the word from this unit that is **most nearly opposite** in meaning to the **boldface** word or expression in the given phrase. Write the word on the line provided.*

16. received a **generous** bequest   _____

17. concluded that the idea was **impracticable**   _____

18. surprised by her **decorous** behavior   _____

19. the commentator's **trenchant** remarks   _____

20. found ourselves in a **secure** position   _____

Choosing the Right Word

*Circle the **boldface** word that more satisfactorily completes each of the following sentences.*

1. Because the speaker before me had defined the topic so narrowly, I had to revise my notes so that only (**apposite, precarious**) data remained.

2. His idea of (**zany, zealous**) behavior at a party is to wear a lampshade as if it were a hat.

3. Every president of our country should renew our determination to create a more (**precarious, viable**) political and social structure for the future.

4. Anyone who spends so many hours a day primping and preening in front of a mirror can only be considered a blatant (**narcissist, zealot**).

5. Although I had no desire to wander through a strange town on foot, I was reluctant to trust my person to the (**vagaries, rapports**) of those wild cab drivers.

6. Even while stressing, as we must, (**utilitarian, narcissistic**) goals, we cannot afford to ignore ethical and aesthetic values.

7. Education is a living process that requires above all a close (**charisma, rapport**) between teacher and student.

8. In condemning their (**apposite, execrable**) conduct, let us not assume that we ourselves are completely free of blame.

9. Their optimism is so unwavering and so all-encompassing that bad news simply fails to (**impinge, bilk**) on their confidence.

10. The disease had such a(n) (**debilitating, execrable**) effect upon her constitution that she was unable to return to work for almost a year.

11. How can you be so easily impressed by those (**vacuous, niggardly**) generalizations and clichés?

12. Succeeding in business is comparable, not to advancing along a straight line, but rather to finding one's way through an uncharted, (**labyrinthine, apposite**) passage.

13. It was the function of a Roman (**augur, zany**) to divine the will of the gods through the interpretation of various natural phenomena, including the flight of birds.

14. I have no sympathy for those who have allowed themselves to be (**impinged, bilked**) by such an obvious get-rich-quick scheme.

15. What we need now is not (**utilitarian, charismatic**) leadership, however inspiring, but steady, modest, and down-to-earth assistance in defining and achieving our goals.

16. True patriotism is a positive attitude, as contrasted with the negative orientation of (**charisma, xenophobia**).

17. When I had lived only a short time in that godforsaken part of the world, I began to realize just how (**vacuous, niggardly**) Nature could sometimes be in bestowing her bounty.

18. With so many rival claimants actively engaged in trying to depose him, the monarch knew that his hold on the throne was at best (**viable, precarious**).

19. A true work of art must be an integrated whole rather than a (**vagary, pastiche**) of discrete or incongruous elements.

20. Your (**xenophobic, zealous**) enthusiasm must be matched by training and discipline if you are to achieve anything worthwhile.

Vocabulary in Context

*Read the following passage, in which some of the words you have studied in this unit appear in **boldface** type. Then complete each statement given below the passage by circling the letter of the item that is **the same** or **almost the same** in meaning as the highlighted word.*

America's Game

(Line)

American football, like soccer and rugby, has its roots in a rough-and-tumble village-against-village game played in the Middle Ages. By the late nineteenth century, football began to look like the game we know today. The system of measured yardage and downs was introduced in 1882. A forward pass was first thrown in the early

(5) twentieth century. The first intercollegiate game was played in 1869, and professional teams were formed in the 1890s. By 1900, football was the country's most popular intercollegiate sport. With popularity, however, came controversy. There was widespread outrage over the game's

(10) violence. Even President Theodore Roosevelt called for change. To answer critics, university presidents formed the National Collegiate Athletic Association in 1906. This group established **viable** rules

(15) to decrease the violence.

In the second half of the twentieth century, professional football's popularity soared, primarily because of television coverage. Electronic scoreboards,

(20) halftime extravaganzas, and sophisticated promotional techniques have broadened the game's appeal and made it even more of a spectacle. The Super Bowl,

Rival high school teams vie for a chance to compete for the state championship.

which determines the professional championship, is perhaps the country's most

(25) watched single athletic event, and college bowls are perennial favorites.

Football today is a big business. Its participants can enjoy huge financial rewards. But it remains a **precarious** game to play. Serious injuries can be as close as the next snap of the ball. Nevertheless, the game is played better than ever, and the players are bigger, stronger, and faster than ever.

(30) Many people complain that football has become too commercial. Many remain disturbed by its aggressiveness and the "win at all costs" approach of coaches and players. Nonetheless, the game continues to gain in popularity. Indeed, football has **impinged** upon baseball's claim as America's pastime. For football fans, after all, it's the game that counts, not the sport's **vagaries** or dangers.

---

1. The meaning of **viable** (line 14) is
a. feasible   c. unworkable
b. stringent   d. simple

2. Precarious (line 27) most nearly means
a. safe   c. risky
b. enjoyable   d. difficult

3. Impinged (line 33) is best defined as
a. stumbled   c. called
b. frowned   d. encroached

4. The meaning of **vagaries** (line 34) is
a. rules   c. scandals
b. quirks   d. finances

Vocabulary for Comprehension

*Read the following passage, in which some of the words you have studied in Units 10–12 appear in **boldface** type. Then answer questions 1–10 on page 139 on the basis of what is <u>stated</u> or <u>implied</u> in the passage and in the introductory statement.*

How and why do great cities develop? This passage looks at the beginnings of New York City.

(Line)

When Henry Hudson returned to Amsterdam in 1610, he informed investors that he had not found a river passage to the Pacific. But he did

(5) report that he sailed into a huge, deep harbor surrounded by rich land, a **sine qua non** for a fur-trading enterprise. Dutch merchants wasted no time. They sent six ships there in

(10) less than two years. Thus, the great city of New York began as a minor trading outpost in the vast Dutch mercantile empire.

For a small country, the Netherlands had big plans—all bottom-line

(15) oriented. It already had holdings in Asia, Africa, and South America. For the Dutch, the New Netherlands colony, headquartered at the foot of

(20) Manhattan, was a venture launched solely to make money for investors. It was managed by the Dutch West India Company. Peter Minuit arrived there to govern in 1626. He quickly

(25) "bought" the island from the Native Americans for goods worth about 60 guilders.

The colony grew slowly, settled by **patricians** through a system whereby

(30) land was deeded to them in return for bringing new settlers. The Dutch traded with the Native Americans, often **bilked** them, and made no effort

to understand them. Worse, albeit

(35) inadvertently, they passed on diseases to which the Native Americans had no resistance.

Manhattan became a cosmopolitan place, home to some 2,000 people

(40) of many backgrounds and religions. But the Dutch forts were weak and no match for the four English warships that sailed into the harbor in 1664. The colony changed hands, becoming the

(45) property of the Duke of York, brother of King Charles II. Changes caused by the takeover were largely **imperceptible**. The colony, now called New York, kept its

(50) multicultural identity and continued to prosper. Although Dutch control lasted only forty years, its impact on the growth of New York as a commercial and cultural center

(55) is undeniable.

1. In the first paragraph (lines 1–13), the author's main focus is on
   a. Dutch trade with the Native Americans in the region of Manhattan
   b. the arrival of Peter Minuit in the New Netherlands colony
   c. the cosmopolitan atmosphere of Manhattan's early years
   d. the importance of Henry Hudson's report to the Dutch when he returned to Amsterdam
   e. the introduction of diseases to which Native Americans had no resistance

2. The meaning of **sine qua non** (line 7) is
   a. task
   b. requisite
   c. plan
   d. preference
   e. charter

3. According to the author, the overriding goal of the Dutch West India Company was to
   a. make money for its investors
   b. compile accurate maps of the coastline
   c. negotiate with the English over the control of Manhattan
   d. explore the region for valuable minerals and timber
   e. set up a New World colony that would compete with the Portuguese

4. Which of the following best explains the author's use of quotation marks around the word *bought* in line 25?
   a. The quotation marks show that the author doubts Peter Minuit bought Manhattan.
   b. The quotation marks imply that the transaction was not a fair one.
   c. The quotation marks signal that this sentence is a flashback.
   d. the quotation marks show that the author has used reliable sources.
   e. The author uses quotation marks to imply that Peter Minuit acted too hastily.

5. **Patricians** (line 29) most nearly means
   a. sailors
   b. farmers
   c. commoners
   d. merchants
   e. aristocrats

6. From the details in paragraph 3 (lines 28–37), you can infer that the attitude of the Dutch settlers toward the Native Americans was
   a. compassionate
   b. ambivalent
   c. polite
   d. exploitative
   e. fearful

7. **Bilked** (line 33) most nearly means
   a. swindled
   b. laughed at
   c. frustrated
   d. charmed
   e. underestimated

8. According to the author, which of the following resulted from the English takeover from the Dutch in 1664?
   a. Manhattan became a less cosmopolitan place.
   b. The fur trade declined.
   c. The colony became known as New York.
   d. The Dutch strengthened their forts.
   e. Closer relations were established with the Native Americans.

9. **Imperceptible** (line 48) is best defined as
   a. immediate
   b. undetectable
   c. obvious
   d. beneficial
   e. disruptive

10. The author's attitude toward the Dutch might best be described as
   a. respectful
   b. apologetic
   c. ironic
   d. factual
   e. disdainful

Grammar in Context

In the sentence "When Henry Hudson returned to Amsterdam in 1610, he informed investors that he had not found a river passage to the Pacific" (lines 1–4 on page 138), the pronoun *he*, which is used twice, has a clear antecedent: *Henry Hudson*. If a pronoun does not have a clear antecedent, however, ambiguity or confusion may result. Clear writers avoid faulty **pronoun reference and shift**.

Ambiguous pronoun reference occurs when a pronoun can refer to either of two antecedents, as in the sentence "The partnership between merchants and investors ended when they felt cheated." *General reference* occurs when a pronoun refers to a general idea rather than to a specific word or phrase, as in "In less than two years, the Dutch sent six ships across the Atlantic, from which a great city grew." *Weak reference* occurs when a pronoun refers to an antecedent that has not been expressed, as in "We spent the day on a bus touring Manhattan, but we didn't photograph a single one." *Indefinite or illogical pronoun shift* occurs when there is an unexpected shift in number or person between a pronoun and its antecedent, as in "Manhattan gradually became a cosmopolitan city, and you could meet people from many different backgrounds there."

On the lines provided, rewrite each of the following sentences, correcting errors in pronoun reference or shift. Write "correct" if the sentence is correct.

1. The Dutch established New York as a small trading outpost. It was a historic beginning for a great city.

_____

_____

2. Henry Hudson reported that he had sailed into a large, deep harbor, which was a necessity for a fur-trading enterprise.

_____

_____

3. In the textbook, they described how Peter Minuit "bought" Manhattan from the Native Americans.

_____

_____

4. The rivalry between the Dutch and the English culminated in the arrival of four of their warships in New York Harbor.

_____

_____

5. Although Dutch control was short-lived, they had a major impact on the growth of the city.

_____

_____

Word Associations

In each of the following groups, circle the word that is best defined or suggested by the given phrase.

1. wrapped in a mystery
a. dichotomy   b. charisma   c. mystique   d. impasse

2. "It seems like they've known each other forever!"
a. narcissism   b. rapport   c. quagmire   d. acumen

3. a magical transformation
a. metamorphosis   b. xenophobia   c. vagary   d. augur

4. an unpredictable event
a. vagary   b. bravado   c. charisma   d. vendetta

5. an official representing the local union at national headquarters
a. patrician   b. raconteur   c. liaison   d. apostate

6. a maze of underground passageways
a. consensus   b. labyrinth   c. non sequitur   d. punctilio

7. a bit of this and a bit of that
a. nihilism   b. apostate   c. metamorphosis   d. pastiche

8. a novel abounding in blood, violence, and weird happenings
a. fulsome   b. apocryphal   c. gothic   d. viable

9. a statement that is not logical
a. non sequitur   b. sine qua non   c. mot juste   d. metamorphosis

10. reminiscent of the Oracle at Delphi
a. raconteur   b. augur   c. patrician   d. lackey

11. a born storyteller
a. liaison   b. zealot   c. lackey   d. raconteur

12. personal magnetism
a. bravado   b. disparity   c. euphoria   d. charisma

13. "Foreigners, go home!"
a. xenophobia   b. impasse   c. narcissism   d. consensus

Choosing the Right Meaning

Read each sentence carefully. Then circle the item that best completes the statement below the sentence.

As we drove into the storm, we were greeted by a staccato drumming produced by marble-size hailstones impinging upon the rooftop of the car.   (2)

1. In line 2 the phrase **impinging upon** most nearly means
a. obtruding upon   b. encroaching upon c. effecting   d. striking

Cosmologists who subscribe to the big bang theory believe that the explosion
from which the universe emerged occurred at least 10 billion years ago but lasted
only a punctilio. (2)

2. The best definition for the word **punctilio** in line 3 is

a. nicety   b. fine point   c. detail   d. instant

Any chef who would venture to cook Asian dishes must be sure to have a supply of
cornstarch, which is employed as a liaison in the preparation of many common sauces. (2)

3. The word **liaison** in line 2 is used to mean

a. intermediary   b. channel   c. thickener   d. contact

A genealogy of the American Whig party would show a final dichotomy in the 1850s,
one branch merging with the newly formed Republican party, the other with the soon-
to-be-extinct Know-Nothing party. (2)

4. In line 1 the word **dichotomy** is used to mean

a. forking   b. schism   c. bifurcation   d. union

Antonyms

*In each of the following groups, circle the word or expression that is
most nearly the **opposite** of the word in **boldface** type.*

1. vacuous
a. incisive
b. cool
c. decisive
d. elderly

2. dissimulate
a. reveal
b. misrepresent
c. organize
d. disrupt

3. flamboyant
a. staid
b. obnoxious
c. harmless
d. immense

4. acumen
a. verbosity
b. sharpness
c. artfulness
d. obtuseness

5. constrict
a. reject
b. disturb
c. expand
d. divide

6. mot juste
a. harangue
b. benefit
c. malapropism
d. desideratum

7. consensus
a. survey
b. agreement
c. beginning
d. disagreement

8. quagmire
a. morass
b. defeat
c. bedrock
d. detour

9. debilitate
a. invigorate
b. enervate
c. remit
d. injure

10. zany
a. daffy
b. impromptu
c. decorous
d. complicated

11. monolithic
a. old-fashioned
b. trite
c. energetic
d. diversified

12. lugubrious
a. melancholy
b. hilarious
c. temporary
d. drowsy

13. niggardly
a. grasping
b. generous
c. uncomfortable
d. pensive

14. execrable
a. commendable
b. intentional
c. indisposed
d. intense

15. viable
a. wordy
b. truthful
c. unworkable
d. practical

16. fulsome
a. repulsive
b. enjoyable
c. complete
d. restrained

17. disparity
a. flaw
b. similarity
c. fusion
d. rationality

18. apposite
a. irrelevant
b. meek
c. mutual
d. similar

19. euphoria
a. charisma
b. narcissism
c. pastiche
d. melancholy

20. bravado
a. vigilance
b. kindness
c. bravery
d. swagger

Completing the Sentence

From the following list of words, choose the one that best completes each of the following sentences. Write the word in the space provided.

apocryphal	disparity	narcissism	quagmire
apposite	empirical	pastiche	raconteur

1. It is sometimes very difficult to tell where self-confidence leaves off and _____ begins.

2. A _____ of old plots and new scandals, this soap opera has little chance of catching on with the viewing public.

3. My hypothesis is based solely on the _____ data collected by reliable observers.

4. I was not pleased to learn that "Washington and the Cherry Tree" is a(n) _____ story.

5. The wily politician hoped to avoid the _____ of controversial social issues in which his opponent had become inextricably mired.

Word Families

A. *On the line provided, write the word you have learned in Units 10–12 that is related to each of the following nouns.*
EXAMPLE: empiricist—**empirical**

1. apocrypha, apocryphalness _____

2. debilitation _____

3. constriction, constrictor _____

4. viability _____

5. monolith _____

6. sublimation _____

7. adjudication _____

8. precariousness _____

9. quixotism, quixotry _____

10. impassibility _____

11. lugubriousness _____

12. disparateness _____

13. niggard _____

14. nihilist _____

15. impingement _____

B. *On the line provided, write the word you have learned in Units 10–12 that is related to each of the following verbs.*

EXAMPLE: metamorphose—**metamorphosis**

16. dichotomize _____

17. execrate _____

18. utilize _____

19. effuse _____

20. perceive _____

 **Two-Word Completions**

Circle the pair of words that best complete the meaning of each of the following passages.

1. When the representatives of labor and management found that they had reached a hopeless _____ in the negotiations for a new contract, they called in an outside mediator to help break the deadlock and _____ the dispute.

a. liaison . . . impinge
b. consensus . . . debilitate
c. rapport . . . dissimulate
d. impasse . . . adjudicate

2. As her _____ lover Aeneas fled her embraces in search of his destiny on the wild and desolate shores of Italy, distraught Queen Dido _____ herself on a huge pyre atop the highest building in Carthage.

a. apocryphal . . . bilked
b. fulsome . . . debilitated
c. apostate . . . immolated
d. execrable . . . adjudicated

3. Throughout the 18th and 19th centuries, the great _____ houses of England were staffed by armies of servants and _____, but today it is impossible for a duke or an earl to keep such a sizable domestic staff.

a. patrician . . . lackeys
b. monolithic . . . apostates
c. gothic . . . zealots
d. utilitarian . . . raconteurs

4. Some anecdotes about historical figures are clearly _____ because they contain _____ and other improbable elements that show the stories were written at a much later date.

a. empirical . . . disparities
b. apocryphal . . . anachronisms
c. utilitarian . . . dichotomies
d. apposite . . . non sequiturs

chron—time

This Greek root appears in **anachronism** (page 117), which means "a misplacing in time of events, objects, customs, or persons in regard to each other." Some other words based on the same root are listed below.

chronically	**chronicler**	**chronology**	**crony**
chronicle	**chronological**	**chronometer**	**cronyism**

From the list of words above, choose the one that corresponds to each of the brief definitions below. Write the word in the blank space in the illustrative sentence below the definition.

1. arranged in order of time or occurrence; relating to or in keeping with the ordering of events in time

This discography is a _____ listing of all the composer's recorded works.

2. one who writes or keeps a record of historical events

That magazine has long been regarded as an astute _____ of fashion.

3. the determination of dates or of the sequence of events; the sequential ordering of dates and events; such a list or table

The CD-ROM provides an accurate _____ of key battles of the last century.

4. an exceptionally accurate clock, watch, or other timepiece

The marine biologist especially values her underwater _____ when she dives.

5. a close friend or companion, chum

They planned an outing at the beach as a casual reunion of their old school _____ .

6. constantly, habitually, over a prolonged period

Despite his responsibility as recording secretary, he is _____ late for meetings.

7. a record of historical events presented in order of occurrence; to make or keep such a record

Anne Frank's poignant _____ of her years in hiding in an Amsterdam attic during World War II has been translated into scores of languages.

8. favoritism shown to old friends or companions in official or political appointments

The search committee accused the dean of _____ in his recent appointments.

From the list of words on page 145, choose the one that best completes each of the following sentences. Write the word in the space provided.

1. Hopelessly poor and _____ ill, the wretched man despaired of ever finding relief from his persistent suffering.

2. The retired senator enjoyed nothing more than to swap stories with a group of his old _____ .

3. The _____ was guaranteed not to deviate more than five seconds from the correct time over the course of a year.

4. The historians Tacitus and Gibbon do not merely _____ events but interpret their meaning and importance as well.

5. Students were given a list of important events in American history and asked to arrange them in correct _____ order.

6. A Benedictine monk, whom we now call the Venerable Bede, was an important _____ of Christianity's growth in Anglo-Saxon England.

7. Police detectives drew up a _____ to show in proper sequence the events leading up to the crime.

8. When the governor began to fill key administration posts with his old business pals, the press accused him of _____ .

---

*Circle the **boldface** word that more satisfactorily completes each of the following sentences.*

1. Writers must decide whether to organize the facts in a paragraph in order of importance, in compare-and-contrast order, or in (**chronological, chronic**) order.

2. The patient's hospital chart includes a highly detailed (**chronometer, chronology**) of her responses to the prescribed course of treatment.

3. Most (**chronometers, chronicles**) rely on the vibrations of a quartz crystal to control the rate at which the time-indicating display moves.

4. I hadn't wanted to attend my twenty-fifth high school reunion; but when I reminisced with my old (**chroniclers, cronies**) at the dinner, I was really glad I had come.

5. After Olaudah Equiano bought his freedom, he became a (**cronyism, chronicler**) of his experiences; his 1789 autobiography was one of the first slave narratives written in English.

6. The Sirens, the Cyclops, and the other mythical beings in Homer's ancient (**cronyism, chronicle**) of Ulysses' adventures continue to inspire writers and filmmakers.

7. If the appointee, a longtime friend of the mayor, is indeed highly qualified, is the accusation of (**cronyism, chronicles**) really justified?

8. The (**chronically, chronologically**) love-struck teen devours romance novels and listens to albums of dreamy music.

Analogies

In each of the following, circle the item that best completes the comparison.

1. rogue is to **picaresque** as
a. mnemonic is to allegorical
b. incubus is to gothic
c. apostate is to epistolary
d. pundit is to historical

2. augur is to **birds** as
a. necromancer is to tea leaves
b. medium is to tarot cards
c. haruspex is to entrails
d. mountebank is to poltergeists

3. dichotomy is to **two** as
a. disparity is to four
b. liaison is to five
c. affinity is to three
d. consensus is to one

4. anachronism is to **time** as
a. malapropism is to tone
b. neologism is to structure
c. solecism is to grammar
d. spoonerism is to accent

5. raconteur is to **anecdotes** as
a. nitwit is to dictums
b. scholar is to tautologies
c. encomiast is to philippics
d. moralist is to homilies

6. quixotic is to **chimerical** as
a. lugubrious is to lachrymose
b. fastidious is to malcontent
c. minuscule is to gargantuan
d. dank is to mellifluous

7. beatitude is to **blissful** as
a. euphoria is to ecstatic
b. despair is to fervid
c. apathy is to disinterested
d. composure is to distraught

8. quagmire is to **morass** as
a. heyday is to decline
b. kudos is to obloquy
c. bane is to nemesis
d. pundit is to proselyte

9. showoff is to **flamboyant** as
a. nihilist is to hidebound
b. apostate is to loyal
c. poltroon is to valiant
d. skinflint is to niggardly

10. patrician is to **aristocracy** as
a. philistine is to bourgeoisie
b. plebeian is to hoi polloi
c. utilitarian is to proletariat
d. sycophant is to elite

Choosing the Right Meaning

Read each sentence carefully. Then circle the item that best completes the statement below the sentence.

The fighting at the Sunken Road during the Battle of Antietam was so sanguine that the site afterward came to be known as Bloody Lane. (2)

1. The word **sanguine** in line 1 most nearly means
a. flushed
b. bloody
c. confident
d. optimistic

The man whom Edgar Allan Poe appointed his literary executor proved to be a malicious sycophant whose baseless slanders gave rise to myths about Poe that have endured to this day. (2)

2. In line 2 the word **sycophant** is used to mean
a. defamer
b. toady
c. flatterer
d. yes-man

Gradually, we came to see that the champion's every move, though apparently vacuous, was in fact in furtherance of a grand design. (2)

3. The word **vacuous** in line 2 most nearly means

a. void   b. fatuous   c. inane   d. purposeless

"People in those old times had convictions; we moderns only have opinions, and
it takes more than a mere opinion to erect a Gothic cathedral."   (2)
       (Heinrich Heine, *The French Stage*)

4. The best definition of the word **Gothic** in line 2 is

a. grotesque   b. sinister   c. gloomy   d. medieval-style

In certain cultures shamans are believed to possess a sort of charisma that permits
them to heal the sick and even communicate with the spirits of the dead.   (2)

5. In line 1 the word **charisma** is used to mean

a. personal magnetism   c. divine gift
b. charm   d. mystique

Two-Word Completions   *Circle the pair of words that best complete the meaning
of each of the following sentences.*

1. Many 18th-century composers merely sketched out the broad outlines of a piece of
music and left the details to the taste and discretion of the individual performer.
Though this system of composition gives the artist considerable latitude for choice
within the _____ of the composer's style, it by no means gives him
or her _____ to change the basic structure, design, or mood of the work.

a. purview . . . pièce de résistance   c. lexicon . . . fait accompli
b. parameters . . . carte blanche   d. matrix . . . mot juste

2. Though human sacrifice was more or less unknown to the Greeks and Romans of
ancient times, many of the barbarian tribes along the borders of the classical world
customarily _____ their angry gods by _____
prisoners of war or other captives on huge pyres erected in sacred groves or other
such places.

a. bruited . . . debauching   c. cozened . . . deracinating
b. lampooned . . . bowdlerizing   d. propitiated . . . immolating

3. Although one of the most learned men of his time, François Rabelais is best known
as a(n) _____ , under the broad, earthy, and often
_____ humor of whose tales lie serious discussions of education,
politics, religion, and philosophy.

a. raconteur . . . ribald   c. homilist . . . maladroit
b. polemicist . . . supine   d. virtuoso . . . tendentious

4. When they're in their cups, some of the _____ denizens of the
local pub become pugnacious, others become sleepy, and still others become
teary-eyed and _____ .

a. hidebound . . . effusive   c. bibulous . . . maudlin
b. bilious . . . waggish   d. malleable . . . contumelious

Enriching Your Vocabulary

Read the passage below. Then complete the exercise at the bottom of the page.

Loanwords from Greek

The Greek language has the longest history among the languages currently spoken in Europe. Throughout its evolution from the fourteenth century B.C. to the present, Greek has developed many words and word parts that English has borrowed to form a vast store of words. In fact, the word *etymology*—the study of word origins—is itself from the Greek *etumologia,* meaning "the true sense of the word."

You may never have studied Greek, visited Greece, or even tasted Greek food. Still, you undoubtedly know quite a few loanwords from that language. In Unit 9, you studied the word *kudos*, meaning "acclaim." *Hedonism* (Unit 8), or "the pursuit of pleasure," comes directly from *hedone*, the Greek word for pleasure. Have you ever experienced a feeling of *euphoria* (Unit 11)? If so, you used a Greek loanword to describe that heady sensation of well-being.

The Greek alphabet is different from the English one. For this reason, some English words derived from Greek exhibit particular spelling traits. For example, consider English words that use the prefix *psych-*, from the Greek word *psyche*, meaning "soul" or "mind." In the word *psychology*, the *p* is silent and the *ch* has a hard /**k**/ sound. Both of these spelling features are consistent with the word's Greek origin.

Psyche Riding a Camel. Bas relief, ca. first century B.C.–third century A.D.

In Column A below are 6 more loanwords from Greek. With or without a dictionary, match each word with its meaning in Column B.

Column A

_____ **1.** aroma
_____ **2.** catastrophe
_____ **3.** catharsis
_____ **4.** climax
_____ **5.** hubris
_____ **6.** phenomenon

Column B

a. the point of greatest intensity in a series of events; to reach or bring about such a point (Greek meaning: *ladder*)

b. a great calamity; total failure; sudden violent change (Greek meaning: *overturning, ruin*)

c. excessive pride, arrogance, or self-confidence (Greek meaning: *insolence, outrage*)

d. any occurrence or fact perceptible to the senses; a marvel; a paragon (Greek meaning: *that which appears*)

e. a pleasant odor that is characteristic of something (Greek meaning: *spice*)

f. a purification or eradication; a figurative release of tension or the emotions (Greek meaning: *purging*)

Definitions

Note carefully the spelling, pronunciation, part(s) of speech, and definition(s) of each of the following words. Then write the word in the blank space(s) in the illustrative sentence(s) following. Finally, study the lists of synonyms and antonyms given at the end of each entry.

1. accolade
(ak' ə lād)

(*n.*) praise or approval; a ceremonial embrace or greeting

The playwright enjoyed the _____ of both the theater critics and the public.

SYNONYMS: kudos, acclaim, cheers, plaudits
ANTONYMS: boos, disapproval, censure, criticism

2. acerbity
(ə sər' bə tē)

(*n.*) sourness or bitterness of taste; harshness or severity of manner or expression

Offended by the _____ of the director's remarks, the actor stormed out of the rehearsal.

SYNONYMS: acidity, astringency, mordancy, asperity
ANTONYMS: blandness, mellowness, mildness

3. attrition
(ə trish' ən)

(*n.*) the process of wearing down by friction or gradual impairment

After many losses due to _____, the weakened army sought an end to hostilities.

SYNONYMS: abrasion, erosion, exhaustion, reduction
ANTONYMS: augmentation, proliferation, enlargement

4. bromide
(brō' mīd)

(*n.*) a trite or commonplace remark; a tiresome or boring person; a sedative

The usual _____ offered by politicians may please crowds but won't solve the nation's problems.

SYNONYMS: cliché, platitude

5. chauvinist
(shō' və nist)

(*adj.*) extravagantly patriotic; blindly devoted to a cause; (*n.*) such a person

During wartime, some newspapers may take an extremely _____ stance in their editorials.

Denying that he is a male _____, the senator cited his record of support for equal rights for women.

SYNONYMS: (*n.*) superpatriot, flag-waver, jingoist

6. chronic
(kron' ik)

(*adj.*) continuing over a long period of time or recurring often

The president set up a blue-ribbon committee to look into the problem of _____ unemployment.

SYNONYMS: recurrent, persistent, inveterate, habitual
ANTONYMS: transitory, transient, sporadic

7. expound
(ek spaünd′)

(*v.*) to explain in detail

The students listened attentively as their physics professor
_____ upon the new theory.

SYNONYMS: elucidate, explicate, delineate

8. factionalism
(fak′ shən əl iz əm)

(*n.*) party strife and intrigue

Because of bitter _____ in both houses
of Congress, no legislation of consequence was passed.

SYNONYMS: infighting, dissension
ANTONYMS: unanimity, harmony, agreement, consensus

9. immaculate
(i mak′ yə lit)

(*adj.*) spotless; without blemish or fault

After I finished washing and waxing my parent's white car, it
was as _____ as new-fallen snow.

SYNONYMS: unsoiled, impeccable
ANTONYMS: blemished, tarnished, stained, sullied

10. imprecation
(im prə kā′ shən)

(*n.*) a curse; the act of cursing

When I found myself stuck in a traffic jam, I could not stop
myself from muttering a few _____.

SYNONYMS: execration, malediction
ANTONYMS: blessing, benediction

11. ineluctable
(in i lək′ tə bəl)

(*adj.*) not able to be avoided, changed, or overcome

Two of life's _____ facts are
death and taxes.

SYNONYMS: unavoidable, inescapable, inevitable
ANTONYMS: avoidable, escapable, reversible, revocable

12. mercurial
(mər kyür′ ē əl)

(*adj.*) characterized by rapid and unpredictable changes of
mood; fickle or inconstant

The temperamental diva is perhaps even more famous for her
_____ behavior than for her voice.

SYNONYMS: erratic, flighty, capricious, volatile
ANTONYMS: phlegmatic, sluggish, constant, steady

13. palliate
(pal′ ē āt)

(*v.*) to make less serious or severe by glossing over; to relieve
without actually curing, mitigate

A few new laws may _____ the
ills that plague our society but will not eradicate them.

SYNONYMS: alleviate, extenuate
ANTONYMS: intensify, magnify, aggravate

14. protocol
(prō' tə kôl)

(*n.*) customs and regulations dealing with official behavior and etiquette, as in a court or among diplomats; a type of international agreement; a memorandum, official account, or record

A breach of _____ at a summit meeting of world leaders can have serious consequences.

SYNONYMS: code of conduct, minutes

15. resplendent
(ri splen' dənt)

(*adj.*) shining or gleaming brilliantly; splendid or magnificent

The knights, clad in _____ armor, rode forth to engage the foe.

SYNONYMS: radiant, dazzling, glorious
ANTONYMS: dull, drab, lusterless

16. stigmatize
(stig' mə tīz)

(*v.*) to brand or mark as in some way discreditable, disgraceful, or ignominious

People sometimes _____ innocent children because of their parents' misdeeds.

SYNONYMS: sully, taint, disgrace
ANTONYMS: whitewash, laud, extol

17. sub rosa
(səb rō' zə)

(*adv.*) in secret; confidentially; privately; (*adj.*) secretive

An unnamed White House source passed crucial information to reporters _____ .

At a series of _____ meetings, the dissenting shareholders planned their next move.

SYNONYMS: (*adv.*) secretly, covertly, stealthily, furtively
ANTONYMS: (*adv.*) overtly, openly

18. vainglory
(vān' glô rē)

(*n.*) excessive pride in and boastfulness about one's own accomplishments or qualities; a vain show or display

With insufferable _____ the young tennis star taunted his opponent after each winning point.

SYNONYMS: vanity, conceit, swagger, pretentiousness
ANTONYMS: humility, modesty, diffidence

19. vestige
(ves' tij)

(*n.*) a trace or visible evidence of something that once existed but now is lost or vanished

The spectacular ruins of the ancient temple are the last _____ of a once-mighty civilization.

SYNONYMS: artifact, relic, remains

20. volition
(vō lish' ən)

(*n.*) the power to choose, will, or decide; the act of choosing, willing, or deciding

Ignoring all my relatives' warnings, I chose the perilous course of my own _____ .

SYNONYMS: free will, choice
ANTONYMS: coercion, compulsion, duress

Completing the Sentence

From the words for this unit, choose the one that best completes each of the following sentences. Write the word in the space provided.

1. Isn't there truly an element of pathos in the certain knowledge that the _____ and overconfidence of our youth will be laid low by "the slings and arrows of outrageous fortune"?

2. You may be scornful about matters of "mere _____," as you call it, but you will soon learn that *how* things are done is often as important as *what* is done.

3. The steady and quiet devotion of people who truly love their country is very different from the noisy fulminations of mindless _____.

4. Despite the heat and the dirt of a summer day in the city, he managed somehow to look cool and _____.

5. The Founding Fathers warned that without an overriding sense of national purpose, this country could be torn apart by _____.

6. His personality was so _____ that we never knew on any given occasion how he would react.

7. Shall I be modest and say that I simply do not deserve these extravagant _____, or shall I be honest and admit that I do?

8. Have we reached the stage where anyone who refuses to go along with the majority is to be _____ as a malcontent?

9. In spite of her advanced age and illness, one could still recognize the _____ of her once ravishing beauty.

10. In an influential book published in 1936, the economist John M. Keynes _____ his theory of the causes of economic collapse.

11. It was a bitter experience to have to leave the village in disgrace, followed by the jeers and _____ of people I had tried to help.

12. Why is it that so many theater critics are noted for the trenchancy of their perceptions and the _____ of their wit?

13. Since we cannot overcome the enemy by direct attack, we will wage a war of _____ against them.

14. No one suggested that I take algebra in my freshman year; I decided to do it purely of my own _____.

15. The agreements that had been concluded _____ by the leaders of both parties aroused a storm of protest when they were finally made public.

16. G. B. Shaw's remark to the effect that "youth is wasted on the young" may be, as you say, an old _____, but it is also profoundly true.

17. Over the years she has tried many different remedies to relieve the pain caused by her _____ arthritis.

18. Many a time-honored home remedy may indeed _____ the symptoms of a disease but do little or nothing to cure it.

19. In the innocent glow of youth and inexperience, we simply assumed that we would be able to avoid the _____ consequences of our own folly.

20. _____ in her first evening gown and her first professional hairdo, she waited impatiently for her date to escort her to the dance.

Synonyms

*Choose the word from this unit that is **the same** or **most nearly the same** in meaning as the **boldface** word or expression in the given phrase. Write the word on the line provided.*

1. preserved the **relics** of an ancient culture _____

2. used one **cliché** after another _____

3. a tirade filled with **maledictions** _____

4. acted of their own **free will** _____

5. **disgraced** because of past mistakes _____

6. an **impeccable** record of service _____

7. asked to **explicate** the meaning of the poem _____

8. accused the candidate of being a **jingoist** _____

9. an organization riven by **dissension** _____

10. known as a **flighty** individual _____

11. ranks depleted by **exhaustion** _____

12. behaved with outrageous **conceit** _____

13. the **inescapable** ravages of time _____

14. helps to **alleviate** the patient's discomfort _____

15. fully complied with the **code of conduct** _____

Antonyms

*Choose the word from this unit that is **most nearly opposite** in meaning to the **boldface** word or expression in the given phrase. Write the word on the line provided.*

16. the unexpected **mildness** of the coach's remarks _____

17. accepted the **criticism** with good grace _____

18. suffers from **sporadic** depression _____

19. discussed the matter **openly** _____

20. clad in **drab** garments _____

Choosing the Right Word

*Circle the **boldface** word that more satisfactorily completes each of the following sentences.*

1. Beneath the (**volition, acerbity**) of their criticism, we recognized a sincere desire to help us solve our problems.

2. My brother's (**chronic, resplendent**) tardiness is constantly getting him into trouble at school.

3. Letting the grim facts speak for themselves, the doctor explained quietly the (**ineluctable, immaculate**) tragedy that results from drug abuse.

4. We spent most of the evening listening to her (**palliate, expound**) on her views on all sorts of interesting subjects.

5. Critics who bestow their (**stigma, accolades**) too easily may gain some quick popularity, but they will soon lose their credibility and influence.

6. Our party can resist the attacks of its enemies from the outside, but it may fall victim to the erosion of (**bromide, factionalism**) from within.

7. His claim to be the "greatest pole-vaulter in the world" would indeed have seemed outrageously (**sub rosa, vainglorious**) if it were not for the fact that he went ahead and proved it.

8. We sought desperately for some new forms of amusement to (**palliate, expound**) the boredom of those endless summer afternoons.

9. George Washington's (**immaculate, mercurial**) reputation as a dedicated patriot has been an inspiration to many generations of Americans.

10. Because the difficulty of the subject matter increases rapidly as the term proceeds, mathematics and physics courses have a high rate of student (**attrition, vainglory**).

11. Although she emphasizes that she was the helpless victim of bad luck, one can recognize the effects of her own (**imprecation, volition**) in bringing about her downfall.

12. In the light of the lessons of history, I am skeptical about the value of any diplomatic conferences held (**sub rosa, ineluctably**).

13. We are all eager to avoid the (**accolade, stigma**) of being prejudiced at the same time that we may be unwilling to purge ourselves of our biases.

14. Although he saw himself as a wit, a bon vivant, and a man-about-town, everyone else regarded him as a hopeless (**factionalism, bromide**).

15. The small bone at the base of the spinal column in humans is thought by biologists to be the (**vestige, accolade**) of a tail.

16. They preceded her to the table, not because (**volition, protocol**) required it, but because they were eager to get at the food.

17. "My country, right or wrong" expresses (**chauvinism, attrition**) in its most common form.

18. Though they are twins, one of them has a highly (**mercurial, vestigial**) temperament, while the other is stolid and reserved.

19. Your threats and (**imprecations, protocols**) leave me unimpressed because I know that your words will not be followed by deeds.

20. His talents, which had seemed so (**vestigial, resplendent**) in his youth, now struck us as unimpressive and even pathetic.

Vocabulary in Context

*Read the following passage, in which some of the words you have studied in this unit appear in **boldface** type. Then complete each statement given below the passage by circling the letter of the item that is **the same** or **almost the same** in meaning as the highlighted word.*

Canyon of Mysteries

(Line)

U.S. Army surveyors made an astonishing discovery when, in 1848, they rode into a deserted canyon in what is now western New Mexico. All around them they saw massive multistory sandstone buildings. They had discovered the center of the vanished Anasazi culture of Chaco Canyon, home to perhaps 5000 people in the early twelfth century. *Anasazi* is a Navajo word meaning "ancient ones" or "ancient strangers." No one knows what these remarkable people called themselves. (5)

The Anasazi left no written records behind. Yet much can be learned about them from the **vestiges** of the **resplendent** structures and the system of roads they built, and from

Remains of multistory Anasazi dwelling at Chaco Canyon

objects and petroglyphs (rock carvings) found at the large number of archaeological sites located in and around the canyon. (10)

The people of Chaco were highly skilled stonemasons. They erected so-called great houses that rose as high as four stories and contained hundreds of rooms and numerous (15) ceremonial chambers called *kivas*. They constructed hundreds of miles of straight roads over uneven terrain. These roads linked some seventy-five outlying settlements to the hub at Chaco. And they did all this (20) without metal tools or the wheel.

The Chacoans found ways to channel water to their land. This enabled them to **palliate** to some extent the difficulties of living in such a harsh and unpredictable climate. But despite such efforts and (25) ceremonies to bring the rains, they found themselves facing **chronic** drought. A prolonged period of scant rainfall beginning around 1130 sent the Chacoan culture into an **ineluctable** decline. By the middle of the century, the great dwellings and little towns were deserted. No one knows where the Anasazi went.

---

1. The meaning of **vestiges** (line 8) is
a. drawings
b. photos
c. remains
d. ruins

2. Resplendent (line 8) most nearly means
a. elaborate
b. large
c. unusual
d. magnificent

3. Palliate (line 24) is best defined as
a. mitigate
b. avoid
c. aggravate
d. analyze

4. The meaning of **chronic** (line 26) is
a. sporadic
b. moderate
c. ruinous
d. persistent

5. Ineluctable (line 28) most nearly means
a. swift
b. inevitable
c. reversible
d. unexpected

 **Definitions**

Note carefully the spelling, pronunciation, part(s) of speech, and definition(s) of each of the following words. Then write the word in the blank space(s) in the illustrative sentence(s) following. Finally, study the lists of synonyms and antonyms given at the end of each entry.

1. accoutrements
(ə kü' trə mənts)

(*n., pl.*) accessory items of clothing or equipment; a soldier's outfit, usually not including arms or clothing; trappings

When the new administration took office, it was accorded all the _____ of power.

SYNONYMS: gear, equipage, appurtenances

2. apogee
(ap' ə jē)

(*n.*) the point in the orbit of a heavenly body or artificial satellite farthest from the earth; the farthest or highest point

Many people consider the works of Michelangelo to represent the _____ of Renaissance art.

SYNONYMS: zenith, apex, summit, pinnacle
ANTONYMS: nadir, bottom, pits, perigee

3. apropos
(ap rə pō')

(*adj.*) appropriate, opportune; (*adv.*) relevantly; incidentally, by the way; speaking of

When choosing a greeting card, I look for the one that is most _____ to the occasion.

_____ of your plans for the summer, where are you going to spend your vacation?

SYNONYMS: (*adj.*) pertinent, germane, apposite, relevant
ANTONYMS: (*adj.*) irrelevant, inappropriate, immaterial

4. bicker
(bik' ər)

(*v.*) to engage in a petty or peevish dispute; to move or run rapidly, rush; to flicker, quiver

If we _____ over every minor detail, we'll never get the job done.

SYNONYMS: squabble, wrangle, quarrel, plash
ANTONYMS: concur, agree, acquiesce

5. coalesce
(kō ə les')

(*v.*) to blend together or fuse so as to form one body or substance

Many small tributaries _____ to form the mighty Amazon River.

SYNONYMS: amalgamate, merge, combine, unite
ANTONYMS: scatter, diffuse, separate

6. contretemps
(kon' trə tän)

(*n.*) an inopportune or embarrassing occurrence; a mishap

I believe in taking life's _____ in my stride rather than making a fuss over them.

SYNONYMS: blunder, mischance, faux pas, gaffe

7. convolution
(kon və lü′ shən)

(*n.*) a rolling up, coiling, or twisting together; a sinuous folding or design

Becase of its many _____, San Francisco's Lombard Street is called "the crookedest street in the world."

SYNONYMS: twist, turn, complication

8. cull
(kəl)

(*v.*) to pick out or select; to gather or collect

I will _____ pertinent quotations from my research to illustrate the point of my paper.

SYNONYMS: glean, choose, pluck

9. disparate
(dis par′ ət) *or*
(dis′ pər it)

(*adj.*) completely distinct or different; entirely dissimilar

Despite our _____ backgrounds and life experiences, we have remained the best of friends.

SYNONYM: divergent
ANTONYMS: similar, homogeneous, uniform

10. dogmatic
(dôg mat′ ik)

(*adj.*) certain of the truth of one's own ideas; inclined to state opinions as if they were indisputable facts

People who are _____ are unlikely to have much tolerance for views that differ from their own.

SYNONYMS: opinionated, doctrinaire, authoritarian
ANTONYMS: open-minded, disinterested, dispassionate

11. licentious
(lī sen′ shəs)

(*adj.*) morally or sexually unrestrained; having no regard for accepted rules, customs, or laws

In *The Lives of the Caesars* the biographer Suetonius describes the emperor Caligula's _____ behavior.

SYNONYMS: wanton, dissolute, lascivious
ANTONYMS: chaste, modest, restrained, prudish

12. mete
(mēt)

(*v.*) to distribute or apportion by or as if by measure; to allot

Part of the job of being a parent is the responsibility to _____ out suitable punishment when a child misbehaves.

SYNONYMS: assign, parcel out

13. noxious
(nok′ shəs)

(*adj.*) harmful to physical health or morals

Firefighters wear respirator masks to protect them from smoke and _____ fumes.

SYNONYMS: pernicious, noisome, deleterious, toxic
ANTONYMS: wholesome, salubrious, beneficial

14. polemic
(pə lem′ ik)

(*n.*) an aggressive attack on or refutation of a specific opinion or doctrine

The columnist was known for his _____ against those at the opposite end of the political spectrum.

SYNONYMS: diatribe, controversy

15. populous
(pop′ yə ləs)

(*adj.*) full of people; filled to capacity; densely populated; having a large population

Millions of people along the _____ Atlantic Coast fled inland as the hurricane approached.

SYNONYMS: crowded, teeming, swarming
ANTONYMS: uninhabited, unpeopled, deserted, barren

16. probity
(prō′ bə tē)

(*n.*) complete and confirmed honesty; total integrity

We should demand that our elected officals conduct themselves with the utmost _____.

SYNONYMS: uprightness, rectitude
ANTONYMS: corruption, venality, immorality, iniquity

17. repartee
(rep ər tē′)

(*n.*) a swift, witty reply; conversation full of such remarks; skill in making such replies or conversation

The writers who made up the famous Algonquin Roundtable were celebrated for their sparkling _____.

SYNONYMS: retort, comeback, banter, verbal sparring

18. supervene
(sü pər vēn′)

(*v.*) to take place or occur as something additional or unexpected; to follow immediately after

Events that none of us could have foreseen in our wildest imaginings _____ to blight our hopes.

SYNONYMS: ensue, succeed
ANTONYMS: precede, antecede

19. truncate
(trən′ kāt)

(*v.*) to shorten by or as if by cutting off, lop

A family emergency forced us to _____ our summer vacation.

SYNONYMS: trim, abbreviate, curtail
ANTONYMS: lengthen, elongate, extend, protract

20. unimpeachable
(ən im pē′ chə bəl)

(*adj.*) beyond doubt or reproach; unquestionable

The members of the jury found the testimony of the key prosecution witness to be _____.

SYNONYMS: irreproachable, irrefutable, unassailable
ANTONYMS: questionable, debatable, dubious

 **Completing the Sentence**

From the words for this unit, choose the one that best completes each of the following sentences. Write the word in the space provided.

1. Our purpose is to help people in trouble, not to _____ out justice like a court of law.

2. After the noisy excitement of the big party, the eerie silence that suddenly _____ seemed unnatural and difficult to accept.

3. They possess the kind of unshakable _____ that not only precludes lying but also requires them to express the truth, no matter what.

4. Although the author's conclusions are open to debate, the scholarship upon which they are based is _____.

5. How can we continue to live in this _____ atmosphere of suspicion and hatred?

6. Though her career in the movies had many ups and downs over the years, it reached its _____ when she won an Academy Award.

7. I hate to _____ with you over the cost of a few gallons of gasoline, but I have to because I don't have a dime to spare.

8. The report was not an impartial assessment of the problems we face; it was an intemperate _____.

9. Although the premier enjoyed all the _____ of high office, in practice he was merely a figurehead who wielded very little power.

10. Does "artistic freedom" justify the making of a movie that is deliberately vulgar and _____ in the hope of cashing in at the box office?

11. From the vast mass of unsolicited manuscripts, the editor _____ the few that might be considered for publication.

12. It was absolutely impossible to follow the _____ of the man's tortuous reasoning as he desperately tried to prove his point.

13. Five minutes after arriving at the dance, I upset the punch bowl—the first of many _____ that made the evening a nightmare.

14. Their respective talents seemed to _____ so that they developed into a well-rounded and highly productive team.

15. True, you did reply to the wisecrack, but I hardly regard "Sez you!" as an outstanding example of devastating _____.

16. Problems such as overcrowding, traffic congestion, and air pollution are more common in big cities than they are in less _____ areas.

17. _____ of your remarks on the probable effect of the law, may I quote from the column of a well-known political commentator?

18. The lower end of the ridge had been somewhat _____ by the action of glacial erosion many thousands of years ago.

19. There are so many _____ elements in her personality that I find it difficult to tell you what kind of person she is.

20. You can't hope to hold a fruitful conversation if you are so _____ that you issue pronouncements instead of offering opinions.

Synonyms

*Choose the word from this unit that is **the same** or **most nearly the same** in meaning as the **boldface** word or expression in the given phrase. Write the word on the line provided.*

1. a hiker's **gear**   _____

2. earned them a reputation for **rectitude**   _____

3. accepted responsibility for the **blunder**   _____

4. began to **squabble** as soon as we sat down _____

5. unprepared for the disaster that **ensued**   _____

6. too **opinionated** to be reasoned with   _____

7. disgusted by their **wanton** behavior   _____

8. amused by their **verbal sparring**   _____

9. **gleaned** a few key ideas from the article   _____

10. **assign** punishments to the guilty parties   _____

11. **combine** to form a united front   _____

12. forced to **curtail** their stay   _____

13. the **toxic** effects of air pollution   _____

14. delivered a **diatribe** against her opponent _____

15. one unexpected **complication** after another _____

Antonyms

*Choose the word from this unit that is **most nearly opposite** in meaning to the **boldface** word or expression in the given phrase. Write the word on the line provided.*

16. a person of **questionable** character   _____

17. responses that are **inappropriate**   _____

18. the **nadir** of the president's popularity rating _____

19. come from **similar** backgrounds   _____

20. visited **uninhabited** islands   _____

 **Choosing the Right Word**

*Circle the **boldface** word that more satisfactorily completes each of the following sentences.*

1. Abraham Lincoln warned that the (**convolutions, dogmas**) of the quiet past were inadequate to the needs of the stormy present.

2. From the roots of ancient prejudices, there grew the (**disparate, noxious**) plants of racial and religious hatreds.

3. The route of the army's retreat was littered with the discarded (**polemics, accoutrements**) of war.

4. We are all imperfect creatures, and none of us has been divinely ordained to (**cull, mete**) out punishment to others for their transgressions.

5. (**Repartee, Supervention**) has been likened to a sort of verbal fencing, with the more skillful contestants driving home their weapons for the kill.

6. Los Angeles recently supplanted Chicago as the second most (**populous, unimpeachable**) city in the United States.

7. Instead of taking a fresh look at the situation, they were satisfied to refute their opponents by repeating old and weary (**polemics, accoutrements**).

8. I had hoped for some understanding and generosity of spirit, not this endless (**bickering, repartee**) over petty details.

9. When we least expected it, a crucial event (**coalesced, supervened**) that changed the outcome of our project.

10. If you are to get along in polite society, you must learn that a remark that is factually true is not necessarily (**populous, apropos**).

11. We must not close our eyes to the flagrant (**disparities, contretemps**) between what our society aspires to be and what it actually is.

12. What they described as a new spirit of freedom and vigorous originality seemed to me mere (**accoutrements, licentiousness**).

13. I agree that it is a very good book, but it is a gross exaggeration to say that it represents the (**apogee, convolution**) of the development of the American novel.

14. "Unless the various factions put aside their differences and (**coalesce, supervene**) into a unified force, we will get absolutely nowhere," I said.

15. Even the most relentless investigations by our political opponents could uncover no evidence that challenged our reputation for (**dogmatism, probity**).

16. We expected a simple explanation, but what we got was an involved rationalization, full of all kinds of strange (**contretemps, convolutions**).

17. The reporter assured her boss that the charges contained in her story were based on information from a(n) (**unimpeachable, noxious**) source.

18. How do you expect to deal with the inevitable problems of life if you raise every (**repartee, contretemps**) to the level of a major tragedy?

19. I have neither the time nor the inclination to plough through those long, dreary books in the hope of (**meting, culling**) a few interesting passages.

20. Because the original article was too long for our needs, we published it in a somewhat (**coalesced, truncated**) form.

Vocabulary in Context

*Read the following passage, in which some of the words you have studied in this unit appear in **boldface** type. Then complete each statement given below the passage by circling the letter of the item that is **the same** or **almost the same** in meaning as the highlighted word.*

Tough Times

(Line)

During the Great Depression, life was especially hard for those living in the panhandle regions of Texas and Oklahoma and in some parts of neighboring states. A severe drought began in 1931 and lasted until 1939. For decades, grasslands had been plowed and planted with wheat; other areas had been
(5) overgrazed. There was nothing to hold the parched soil in place. The consequences were devastating. Powerful winds blew across the land, sweeping up the loose topsoil into great, rolling clouds of dust that people called "black
(10) blizzards." Acres of farmland and pastures were destroyed, and cattle died by the thousands. Banks foreclosed mortgages on farm after farm. The area became known as the Dust Bowl.

More than two million of the region's inhabitants
(15) were forced to leave their homes. These people, mostly dispossessed farmers, piled their meager belongings into their cars and trucks and headed west in the largest migration in American history. Many went to California, hoping to find work in the
(20) state's orchards and cotton fields, but their hopes for a fresh start were cruelly **truncated**. Instead of opportunities, they found squalid, **populous** labor

Dorothea Lange's camera captured the suffering of migrant workers.

camps crammed with poor, desperate migrants like themselves. Living conditions in the camps were **noxious**. There was no sanitation or electricity, and outbreaks of
(25) diseases such as typhoid, smallpox, and tuberculosis were common. People **bickered** and competed for the few low-paying jobs the larger growers made available. It was a terrible time indeed.

Some of America's finest artists chronicled the suffering of the migrants during these terrible years. John Steinbeck's novels, Woody Guthrie's songs, and Dorothea
(30) Lange's photographs poignantly captured the human drama of the Dust Bowl era.

---

1. The meaning of **truncated** (line 21) is
a. mocked
b. curtailed
c. protracted
d. revised

2. Populous (line 22) most nearly means
a. deserted
b. makeshift
c. filthy
d. teeming

3. Noxious (line 24) is best defined as
a. pernicious
b. repugnant
c. salubrious
d. dangerous

4. The meaning of **bickered** (line 26) is
a. languished
b. quarreled
c. joked
d. schemed

Definitions

Note carefully the spelling, pronunciation, part(s) of speech, and definition(s) of each of the following words. Then write the word in the blank space(s) in the illustrative sentence(s) following. Finally, study the lists of synonyms and antonyms given at the end of each entry.

1. adumbrate
(ad′ əm brāt)

(v.) to outline or sketch broadly; to foreshadow or prefigure; to disclose partially

Writers often _____ key ideas right away and then elaborate on them later.
SYNONYM: indicate

2. apotheosis
(ə poth ē ō′ sis)

(n.) the elevation of a person to a divine rank or status; the glorification of a person as an ideal; a glorified ideal

Medieval knights were fierce warriors, but in literature they are presented as the _____ of chivalry.
SYNONYM: deification

3. ascetic
(ə set′ ik)

(adj.) practicing strict self-denial for the sake of personal or spiritual discipline; (n.) one who leads a life of self-discipline, especially to express religious devotion

Some artists and writers may find it beneficial to lead an _____ life free of distractions.

The life of an _____ repays the sacrifice of wordly things with profound spiritual rewards.
SYNONYMS: (adj.) austere, spartan; (n.) celibate
ANTONYMS: (adj.) wanton, dissolute; (n.) hedonist

4. bauble
(bô′ bəl)

(n.) a small, showy ornament of little value or use

I found a rather valuable piece of vintage costume jewelry among the _____ at the yard sale.
SYNONYMS: trifle, gewgaw, knickknack, bagatelle
ANTONYMS: gem, precious jewel, treasure

5. beguile
(bi gīl′)

(v.) to mislead or deceive; to cheat; to divert; to cause to vanish unnoticed

Many travelers choose to _____ away the long hours of a journey with an absorbing book.
SYNONYMS: delude, dupe, lure, while away

6. burgeon
(bər′ jən)

(v.) to put forth new buds, leaves, or greenery; to develop rapidly or suddenly

Though it was still winter according to the calendar, our garden _____ in the warm, sunny weather.
SYNONYMS: sprout, blossom, bloom, flourish
ANTONYMS: atrophy, wither, shrivel, diminish

7. complement
(kom′ plə mənt)

(*n.*) something that completes a whole; the quantity or number needed to make up a whole; the full number or allowance; (*v.*) to complete

The full _____ of dignitaries was present for the president's State of the Union Address.

She chose a hat that _____ her new outfit.

SYNONYMS: (*n.*) balance; (*v.*) round out

8. contumacious
(kon tü mā′ shəs)

(*adj.*) obstinately or willfully disobedient; openly rebellious

Teenagers who are eager to assert their independence may become quite _____ at times.

SYNONYMS: impudent, unruly, defiant, refractory
ANTONYMS: docile, meek, deferential, cooperative

9. curmudgeon
(kər məj′ ən)

(*n.*) an irascible, churlish person

No matter how hard we try, nothing we do seems to please our _____ of a boss.

SYNONYMS: grouch, crank, sorehead, churl

10. didactic
(dī dak′ tik)

(*adj.*) intended to instruct, especially morally; inclined to moralize too much

At its best, children's literature teaches values, making it _____ as well as entertaining.

SYNONYMS: educational, instructional, moralistic

11. disingenuous
(dis in jen′ yü əs)

(*adj.*) lacking in sincerity or candor

_____ individuals sometimes betray themselves in the very act of trying to appear sincere.

SYNONYMS: artful, sly, two-faced, insincere
ANTONYMS: candid, frank, artless, sincere

12. exculpate
(ek′ skəl pāt)

(*v.*) to clear of guilt or blame

"I will present irrefutable evidence," the lawyer declared, "that will _____ my client."

SYNONYMS: absolve, exonerate, acquit
ANTONYMS: convict, condemn

13. faux pas
(fō pä′)

(*n.*) a slip in manners or conduct; a social blunder

No sooner had I arrived at the party than I embarrassed myself by committing a dreadful _____.

SYNONYMS: indiscretion, gaffe
ANTONYMS: coup, tour de force

14. fulminate
(ful′ mə nāt)

(*v.*) to denounce or condemn vehemently; to explode, detonate

The senator proceeded to _____
against foreign commitments and entanglements.

SYNONYMS: rail, inveigh
ANTONYMS: praise, applaud, commend, extol

15. fustian
(fəs′ chən)

(*n.*) inflated or pretentious language in speech or writing; a cloth made of cotton and flax

Although the politician's speech was filled with bombast and
_____, it was devoid of substance.

SYNONYMS: rant, claptrap, bombast, grandiloquence

16. hauteur
(hô tûr′)

(*n.*) haughtiness of bearing or attitude

His cold _____ and disdainful
attitude made him extremely unpopular with his colleagues.

SYNONYMS: conceit, superciliousness, snobbishness
ANTONYMS: modesty, humility, diffidence, mousiness

17. inhibit
(in hib′ it)

(*v.*) to restrain or hold back; to hinder or arrest; to prohibit

Poor eating habits may _____ a
young person's physical development.

SYNONYMS: repress, check, suppress
ANTONYMS: foster, promote, expedite, facilitate

18. jeremiad
(jer ə mī′ əd)

(*n.*) an elaborate or prolonged lamentation; any tale of woe

When asked about their sad plights, talk show guests often
launch into tearful _____.

ANTONYMS: paean, song of praise

19. opportunist
(op ər tü′ nist)

(*n.*) one who makes a practice of taking advantage of circumstances to further his or her own self-interest, regardless of principles or ultimate consequences

_____ tend to treat those who are
not useful to them with callous indifference.

SYNONYMS: self-seeker, exploiter

20. unconscionable
(ən kon′ shən ə bəl)

(*adj.*) not guided or restrained by conscience, prudence, or reason; unscrupulous; immoderate

Top management's looting of the employees' retirement fund
can only be described as _____.

SYNONYMS: unjustifiable, indefensible, unforgivable
ANTONYMS: justifiable, reasonable, honorable

Completing the Sentence

From the words for this unit, choose the one that best completes each of the following sentences. Write the word in the space provided.

1. What at first appeared to be no more than a rather favorable opinion of himself has _____ into a seemingly unlimited conceit.

2. Her standards of proper behavior are so demanding that she regards every minor _____ as an unforgivable social offense.

3. In a rather silly painting called *The* _____ *of Homer*, the artist attempts to show the blind poet's reception among the gods.

4. I wonder how many people have been taken in by those silly TV ads that attempt to pass off worthless _____ as valuable jewelry.

5. The editorial argues that the crime-fighting situation cannot improve until the police department receives its full _____ of personnel.

6. How could a person of your knowledge and experience allow yourself to be _____ by vague promises and empty reassurances?

7. While two of the accused were indicted on conspiracy charges, the third was eventually _____ of any involvement in the plot.

8. It is often more effective to offer a few just words of criticism than to _____ long and loud against those who offend us.

9. Because there was no time to go into elaborate details, all that we could do was to _____ the general features of the plan.

10. Instead of simply stating his case, he launched into an emotional appeal whose language degenerated into mere _____ and bombast.

11. I won't go into that shop because the snooty salespeople treat me with the _____ and disdain of aristocrats dealing with their lackeys.

12. Successful politicians must be alert to take advantage of every favorable circumstance, but if they are no more than _____, it is hard to see how they will ever accomplish anything worthwhile.

13. After his conversion, the young man renounced his former profligacy and dissipation to lead the life of a(n) _____ .

14. I find it impossible to understand how the world can stand idly by while _____ acts of cruelty are being committed daily.

15. Though your unwillingness to make me a small loan is disappointing, what infuriates me is your _____ explanation that it is "for my own good."

16. At first we thought that he was just pretending to be surly, but later we discovered that he really was a(n) _____ .

17. What we need in this situation is not a lugubrious _____ cataloging our troubles but a workable plan for improvements.

18. The chairman of the Senate committee angrily threatened the witness with contempt charges because of her _____ attitude.

19. For the eighteenth-century moralist, art and literature had an essentially _____ purpose; they should teach as well as entertain.

20. We all have aggressive impulses, but in most cases our early training and conditioning tend to _____ the open expression of them.

Synonyms

*Choose the word from this unit that is **the same** or **most nearly the same** in meaning as the **boldface** word or expression in the given phrase. Write the word on the line provided.*

1. mocked the orator's **grandiloquence** _____

2. led an **austere** existence _____

3. **misled** unwary customers with vague promises _____

4. **rounded out** the meal perfectly _____

5. **outlined** their plans at a press conference _____

6. committed one **gaffe** after another _____

7. will **exonerate** them without further ado _____

8. the **deification** of the emperor _____

9. **flourished** in that mild climate _____

10. **rails** against the government's policies _____

11. **knicknacks** that have great sentimental value _____

12. has a reputation for being a **grouch** _____

13. listened patiently to my friend's **tale of woe** _____

14. dismissed as **moralistic** by most literary critics _____

15. regaded as a ruthless **exploiter** _____

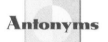

Antonyms

*Choose the word from this unit that is **most nearly opposite** in meaning to the **boldface** word or expression in the given phrase. Write the word on the line provided.*

16. a group of **docile** individuals _____

17. considered their actions **justifiable** _____

18. gave a **sincere** answer to the question _____

19. surprised by the celebrity's **diffidence** _____

20. conditions that **foster** economic growth _____

Choosing the Right Word

*Circle the **boldface** word that more satisfactorily completes each of the following sentences.*

1. When you have been guilty of rude conduct, don't try to minimize your guilt by referring to the incident as a mere (**jeremiad, faux pas**).

2. You are too young to understand how the trials of life can transform a happy-go-lucky youth into a solitary (**bauble, curmudgeon**).

3. The situation was rapidly becoming intolerable because some of the club members were not merely uncooperative but positively (**contumacious, opportunist**).

4. You have written a(n) (**didactic, unconscionable**) novel with a wealth of authentic documentation, but you have forgotten to entertain your readers.

5. (**Beguiled, Burgeoned**) by high-pressure sales talk, I bought a car that I did not need, could not afford, and did not even know how to drive.

6. The author found it ironic that the novel he had tossed off in his youth as a mere (**bauble, complement**) came to be viewed as his masterpiece.

7. The aim of the new biography was to (**exculpate, inhibit**) its subject of charges that previous biographers had wrongfully pressed against him.

8. What is the basis for your statement that advertising costs account for an (**ascetic, unconscionable**) part of the retail price of many products?

9. Many historians believe those apparently minor incidents (**adumbrated, exculpated**) the great revolutionary uprising that occurred a few years later.

10. In a democracy we have no need to disguise the human failings of our leaders; we can respect them without (**beguiling, apotheosizing**) them.

11. The candidates underrate the electorate if they think they can win votes with that kind of antiquated (**curmudgeon, fustian**).

12. What disappointed me was not so much your failure to complete the job but your (**didactic, disingenuous**) efforts to avoid all responsibility for the debacle.

13. Even the innate talents of a Mozart or an Einstein cannot (**fulminate, burgeon**) unless the environment is favorable to their growth.

14. Unlike the Athenians, who delighted in luxury, the Spartans espoused the virtue of (**ascetic, fustian**) simplicity.

15. The speaker referred scornfully to the "hysterical (**jeremiads, hauteurs**) of the ecologists," but I believe that they are warning us of real dangers.

16. I must say that I agree with their (**inhibitions, fulminations**) against those who deface our public buildings with unsightly graffiti.

17. They make an excellent team because his deftness in handling people effectively (**complements, adumbrates**) her remarkable executive abilities.

18. When I asked him if he could dance, he looked at me with supreme (**disingenuousness, hauteur**) and said, "Could Caruso sing?"

19. Your tactics prove that you are not just an (**opportunist, apotheosis**) but someone with a ruthless disregard for others.

20. Since you are usually a rather boisterous person, I was surprised by your (**ascetic, inhibited**) behavior at the party.

Read the following passage, in which some of the words you have studied in this unit appear in **boldface** type. Then complete each statement given below the passage by circling the letter of the item that is **the same** or **almost the same** in meaning as the highlighted word.

Genius Rediscovered

(Line)

Zora Neale Hurston, folklorist, novelist, and anthropologist, once said that "the world is to the strong." She did not let anything **inhibit** her talent and ambition. Young Zora was raised in Eatonville, Florida, the first incorporated black community in America. Life in Eatonville had a profound impact on her character and her writing. The town was self-sufficient and largely free of racial prejudice. (5) African American culture thrived there.

Hurston attended Howard University and published her first story in the school's literary magazine in 1921. In 1925, she moved to New York City. There the outspoken and spirited Zora became a part of the flourishing Harlem Renaissance. She studied anthropology at Barnard College on a scholarship, concentrating on (10) African American folklore. In 1929, she returned to the South to do field research.

Hurston spent six years listening and learning. Her research provided her with material for a number of folklore collections, (15) beginning with *Mules and Men* (1935). She also continued to write fiction, publishing her most famous novel, *Their Eyes Were Watching God*, in 1938. Hurston's works are rich portrayals of life in black communities and capture the (20) authentic dialect of the people who lived in them. Although she broke new ground in the field of ethnography by employing literary techniques, little of her output was appreciated during her lifetime. Hurston's writing style (25)

Zora Neale Hurston (1891–1960)

disturbed many of her contemporaries. They **fulminated** against her re-creation of the oral culture and dismissed her writings as reactionary. The novelist Richard Wright likened her portrayals of African Americans to minstrel shows.

After her death, however, her talents were reassessed. Writers such as Alice Walker praised her as a pioneer. A new generation of readers and critics **exculpated** Hurston (30) of the charge that her work was offensive, and her reputation **burgeoned**. Many of her works now appear in literature texts and in anthologies of African American writings.

---

1. The meaning of **inhibit** (line 2) is
  a. conceal   c. shape
  b. restrain   d. foster

2. Fulminated (line 26) most nearly means
  a. demonstrated   c. railed
  b. argued   d. voted

3. Exculpated (line 30) is best defined as
  a. exonerated   c. accused
  b. condemned   d. indicted

4. The meaning of **burgeoned** (line 31) is
  a. flourished   c. grew
  b. stagnated   d. diminished

Visit us at www.sadlier-oxford.com for interactive puzzles and games.

REVIEW UNITS 13–15

Vocabulary for Comprehension

*Read the following passage, in which some of the words you have studied in Units 13–15 appear in **boldface** type. Then answer questions 1–11 on page 172 on the basis of what is <u>stated</u> or <u>implied</u> in the passage and in the introductory statement.*

Even harzardous jobs have their satisfactions, as this passage makes clear.

(Line)

Birds aren't the only ones who can enjoy a bird's-eye view of things. The intrepid workers who wash the windows of skyscrapers and other

(5) tall buildings share that lofty position.

Working hundreds of feet above the sidewalk is not for everybody, certainly not for anyone who is **inhibited** by a fear of heights. But

(10) heights are just one of the hazards faced by window washers. **Mercurial** weather conditions also put workers at risk. They must learn to deal calmly and cautiously with wind and rain and

(15) snow. They deserve our praise for their courage and the skill with which they do their difficult job.

Tall buildings have various kinds of windows. Some can be cleaned

(20) while the worker stands inside the building. Others can be opened halfway or tilted inward and cleaned by leaning out while remaining inside. Still others cannot be opened

(25) and must be cleaned from the outside. To do this, workers may have to stand on a narrow ledge or on a platform that is suspended by cables from a building's roof.

(30) Workers wear safety harnesses that they secure to the window frames while they use their squeegees to clean the glass. Window washers

also need gloves, safety goggles,

(35) and respirator masks to protect them from caustic cleaning substances. Most important of all, they should always check their equipment before beginning work to

(40) make sure that everything is in good condition and fastened securely.

People who become window washers generally do so of their own **volition**. They say that the perks of

(45) the job outweigh the dangers. First of all there is the satisfaction of keeping windows **immaculate**. Then, of course, there are those bird's-eye views. Window washers

(50) can look out over the **resplendent** tops of magnificent tall buildings gleaming in the sunlight and enjoy the panorama of the city.

1. The first paragraph (lines 1–5) introduces the topic of the passage with which of the following?
   a. a statistic
   b. an anecdote
   c. a quotation
   d. an analogy
   e. a symbol

2. The meaning of **inhibited** (line 9) is
   a. made dizzy
   b. held back
   c. prohibited
   d. unnerved
   e. unconcerned

3. **Mercurial** (line 11) most nearly means
   a. volatile
   b. flighty
   c. stormy
   d. predictable
   e. unseasonable

4. Based on the details cited by the writer in paragraph 2 (lines 6–17), which of the following pairs of qualities are most needed by window washers?
   a. intelligence and a sense of humor
   b. humility and politeness
   c. compassion and restraint
   d. foresight and initiative
   e. calmness and caution

5. According to the passage, all the following are related to window washers' safety EXCEPT
   a. respirator masks
   b. harnesses
   c. squeegees
   d. goggles
   e. equipment checks

6. The meaning of **volition** (line 44) is
   a. compulsion
   b. need
   c. whim
   d. choice
   e. ability

7. **Immaculate** (line 47) most nearly means
   a. spotless
   b. sealed
   c. safe
   d. soiled
   e. faultless

8. Which of the following best states the main idea of paragraph 4 (lines 42–53)?
   a. The satisfactions of window washing outweigh the dangers.
   b. Accidents in such a dangerous job are inevitable.
   c. Window washers perform hazardous work for very low pay.
   d. Many window washers have an artistic temperament.
   e. Most window washers are devoted to their work.

9. At the end of the passage, which of the following provides an echo of the introduction in the first paragraph?
   a. a reference to unpredictable weather conditions
   b. mention of the sacrifices made by window washers
   c. a reference to enjoyment of bird's-eye views
   d. mention of the importance of safety equipment
   e. an anecdote about everyday urban life

10. **Resplendent** (line 50) is best defined as
    a. dramatic
    b. decorative
    c. grimy
    d. dazzling
    e. varied

11. Which of the following best describes the writer's attitude toward the subject matter of the passage?
    a. informal
    b. enthusiastic
    c. humorous
    d. skeptical
    e. critical

Grammar in Context

In the sentence "They must learn to deal calmly and cautiously with wind and rain and snow" (lines 13–15 on page 171), the adverbs "calmly" and "cautiously" exhibit parallel structure, as do the nouns "wind," "rain," and "snow." **Parallel structure** is the use of the same grammatical form for equal ideas. If the author had written "calmly and with caution," the sentence would have contained **faulty parallelism**. In order to ensure clear meaning and smooth rhythm in your sentences, you should avoid faulty parallelism.

To create parallel structure, pair a noun with a noun, a prepositional phrase with a prepositional phrase, an infinitive with an infinitive, a noun clause with a noun clause, and so on. For example, the following senentece contains faulty parallelism: "Their routine procedure is to check safety harnesses and the evaluation of respirator masks." To correct the sentence, use an infinitive with an infinitive: "Their routine procedure is <u>to check</u> safety harnesses and <u>to evaluate</u> respirator masks." Sometimes you need to repeat an article, a preposition, or a pronoun before each of the parallel elements in order to make your meaning clear. To correct the faulty parallilism in "Workers may have to stand on a narrow ledge or suspended platform," repeat the preposition "on" and the article "a."

On the lines provided, rewrite each of the following sentences to correct faulty parallelism. Write "correct" if the sentence is correct.

1. Working hundreds of feet in the air is not for everybody, certainly not anyone afraid of heights.

   _____

   _____

2. To wear safety equipment and coping with hazards calmly are important requirements for the job of window washer.

   _____

   _____

3. Window washers deserve our praise for their courage and because they are skillful.

   _____

   _____

4. Unpredictable weather conditions may include rain, snow, and windy.

   _____

   _____

5. The equipment needed to protect workers from caustic substances includes gloves, goggles, and masks.

   _____

   _____

6. A final check before work ensures safety and that the equipment is reliable.

   _____

   _____

In each of the following groups, circle the word that is best defined or suggested by the given phrase.

1. "May you never have a moment's peace!"
 a. bromide   b. imprecation   c. polemic   d. vestige

2. "By the way . . . "
 a. chronic   b. contumacious   c. apropos   d. unconscionable

3. put his foot in his mouth
 a. protocol   b. faux pas   c. fustian   d. jeremiad

4. infighting among the company's directors
 a. factionalism   b. convolution   c. contretemps   d. probity

5. told a story to teach a moral
 a. populous   b. unconscionable   c. didactic   d. chauvinist

6. put off by their snootiness
 a. apotheosis   b. repartee   c. vainglory   d. hauteur

7. not interested in the opinions of others
 a. ascetic   b. dogmatic   c. disparate   d. sub rosa

8. their greatest moment
 a. acerbity   b. accolade   c. apogee   d. imprecation

9. the usual collection of platitudes
 a. bromide   b. jeremiad   c. apotheosis   d. volition

10. squabble over trifles
 a. expound   b. stigmatize   c. bicker   d. coalesce

11. as honest as the day is long
 a. accoutrements   b. chauvinist   c. vestige   d. probity

12. soften the impact
 a. coalesce   b. expound   c. truncate   d. palliate

Choosing the Right Meaning

Read each sentence carefully. Then circle the item that best completes the statement below the sentence.

"I have seen
A curious child, who dwelt upon a tract   (2)
Of inland ground, applying to his ear
The convolutions of a smooth-lipped shell,   (4)
To which, in silence hushed, his very soul
Listened intensely."   (6)
        (William Wordsworth, *The Excursion*)

1. In line 4 the word **convolutions** most nearly means
 a. complications   b. sounds   c. coils   d. openings

Judging by the cool embrace and the perfunctory kiss, neither party found the
accolade particularly agreeable. (2)

2. In line 2 the word **accolade** most nearly means

a. praise   b. greeting   c. cheers   d. acclaim

Purported to be the memoranda of a series of conspirational meetings between
Jews and Freemasons, the *Protocols of the Elders of Zion* were in fact forgeries (2)
concocted by the Russian secret police.

3. The word ***Protocols*** in line 2 is used to mean

a. regulations   b. agreements   c. codes   d. minutes

Doctors were at a loss to account for the malady, which was as remarkable for its
virulence as for the suddenness with which it fulminated. (2)

4. The word **fulminated** in line 2 is used to mean

a. detonated   b. denounced   c. exploded   d. railed against

 **Antonyms**   *In each of the following groups, circle the word or expression that is
most nearly the **opposite** of the word in **boldface** type.*

1. truncate
a. unpack
b. elongate
c. embark
d. shorten

2. sub rosa
a. secretly
b. overtly
c. repeatedly
d. illegally

3. exculpate
a. acquire
b. bury
c. deactivate
d. convict

4. acerbity
a. slander
b. asperity
c. mildness
d. uncertainty

5. immaculate
a. stained
b. restrained
c. satirical
d. impeccable

6. populous
a. deserted
b. teeming
c. unknown
d. urban

7. noxious
a. deleterious
b. arrogant
c. wholesome
d. isolated

8. contumacious
a. refractory
b. hungry
c. ardent
d. docile

9. burgeon
a. relieve
b. rest
c. atrophy
d. flourish

10. apropos
a. irrelevant
b. pertinent
c. common
d. exotic

11. licentious
a. aggressive
b. chaste
c. humorous
d. legal

12. disingenuous
a. artless
b. dissembling
c. resilient
d. resourceful

13. ascetic
a. austere
b. fit
c. dissolute
d. sedentary

14. ineluctable
a. tolerant
b. avoidable
c. distorted
d. fragile

15. bicker
a. argue
b. select
c. agree
d. drive

16. inhibit
a. suppress
b. desert
c. promote
d. dwell

17. disparate
a. divergent
b. employable
c. similar
d. distant

18. mercurial
a. lovable
b. sluggish
c. disdainful
d. capricious

19. unimpeachable
a. irrefutable
b. partisan
c. obligatory
d. questionable

20. factionalism
a. bigotry
b. multiplication
c. discord
d. unanimity

Completing the Sentence

From the following list of words, choose the one that best completes each of the following sentences. Write the word in the space provided.

apogee	coalesce	opportunist	repartee
beguile	fustian	protocol	volition

1. "Now that I'm at the _____ of my career," the actress said, "I guess I have nowhere to go from here but down."

2. No one told me to go out for the football team; I did it entirely of my own _____ .

3. "_____ requires that I report to the foreign office as soon as I arrive," the diplomat observed.

4. His speeches are filled with _____ and bombast—in sharp contrast to the subdued, constructive comments of his opponent.

5. He is too much of a(n) _____ to be relied upon to stay with us when the other side begins to move ahead.

Word Families

A. *On the line provided, write the word you have learned in Units 13–15 that is related to each of the following nouns.*

EXAMPLE: supervention—**supervene**

1. license, licentiousness _____

2. contumacy _____

3. disparateness _____

4. inhibition, inhibitor _____

5. population, populace, populousness _____

6. exculpation _____

7. palliation, palliator _____

8. fulmination _____

9. mercury, mercurialness _____

10. stigma, stigmatization, stigmatic _____

11. didact, didacticism, didactics _____

12. resplendence, resplendency _____

13. beguilement, beguiler _____

14. ineluctability _____

15. disingenuousness _____

B. *On the line provided, write the word you have learned in Units 13–15 that is related to each of the following verbs.*
EXAMPLE: apotheosize—**apotheosis**

16. impeach _____

17. polemicize _____

18. dogmatize _____

19. acerbate _____

20. convolute _____

 **Two-Word Completions**

Circle the pair of words that best complete the meaning of each of the following passages.

1. In the 18th century, all art had two _____ purposes: "to point a moral or adorn a tale." Accordingly, no work was judged to be really complete if either the _____ or the decorative element was not in evidence.
a. vestigial . . . dogmatic
b. ineluctable . . . licentious
c. complementary . . . didactic
d. unimpeachable . . . chauvinistic

2. "The man is not a disinterested observer of the passing scene," I said. "He is essentially a(n) _____ who uses his column in the newspaper as a kind of soapbox from which to _____, like some Old Testament prophet, against the iniquities of those around him."
a. curmudgeon . . . exculpate
b. chauvinist . . . palliate
c. opportunist . . . truncate
d. polemicist . . . fulminate

3. During the election of 1860, the Democrats could not present a united front because the party was torn asunder by _____ strife and petty regional _____.
a. factional . . . bickering
b. contumacious . . . attrition
c. dogmatic . . . repartee
d. unconscionable . . . vainglory

4. During the Civil War, Robert E. Lee's freedom of choice was seriously _____ by the fact that the South could never replace the losses it sustained through normal battlefield _____.
a. palliated . . . volition
b. inhibited . . . attrition
c. truncated . . . convolution
d. adumbrated . . . imprecation

Building with Classical Roots

temp—time

This Latin root appears in **contretemps** (page 157), which means "an inopportune or embarrassing mishap." Some other words based on the same root are listed below.

contemplative	extempore	temperance	tempest
contemporaneous	temperamentally	temperature	tempestuous

From the list of words above, choose the one that corresponds to each of the brief definitions below. Write the word in the blank space in the illustrative sentence below the definition.

1. the degree of hotness or coldness in a body or an environment; the specific degree of hotness or coldness as measured on a scale

The parents worried when the baby continued to run a high _____ for three days.

2. stormy; violent; turbulent

Their _____ relationship ended when the stress became just too much to bear.

3. existing or occurring at the same period of time

The lives of writer Christopher Marlowe and Sir Walter Raleigh were _____ with that of William Shakespeare.

4. a violent storm; a tumult, uproar

The small fishing boat foundered in the raging _____.

5. inclined to consider intently, thoughtful; meditative; pensive

Rodin's famed sculpture *The Thinker* shows a man sitting in a(n) _____ pose.

6. in an impromptu, unrehearsed manner; on the spur of the moment

After hearing the mayor's disturbing statement, an irate citizen delivered a rebuttal _____.

7. by nature, disposition; moodily; impulsively

Although she had always dreamed of being an investigative journalist, she soon realized that she was _____ unsuited for the job.

8. moderation, self-restraint; total abstinence from alcohol

My brother, a cautious person, follows the path of _____ in all areas of life.

From the list of words on page 178, choose the one that best completes each of the following sentences. Write the word in the blank space provided.

1. After the _____ events of the French Revolution and Napoleonic Wars, Europe settled down to an era of relative peace and quiet.

2. Shakespeare portrays Richard II as more a poet than a prince, and on that account _____ unfit to rule England.

3. You may regard the controversy as one of far-reaching importance, but in my opinion it is merely another _____ in a teacup.

4. The Restoration Period in England was roughly _____ with the start of the reign of Louis XIV in France.

5. Once we learned that we were both competing for the one remaining opening on the roster, the _____ of our friendship began to cool noticeably.

6. Her memorial tribute to the departed hero was all the more moving because it was delivered _____ rather than from prepared notes.

7. Her hatchet raids on saloons made Carrie Nation one of the most celebrated crusaders of the _____ movement.

8. In his *Portrait of a Woman Deep in Thought*, the painter has magically captured his subject's _____ mood.

---

*Circle the **boldface** word that more satisfactorily completes each of the following sentences.*

1. At the party, one of the guests gave a hilarious (**extempore, temperamental**) imitation of the rock star whose hit song came on the radio as we were leaving.

2. Some people find it far easier to stick to complete self-denial in certain cases than to practice (**tempest, temperance**).

3. Rare books and letters will last longer if they can be kept in an environment whose humidity and (**temperance, temperature**) levels are carefully controlled.

4. The photographer's most famous work shows a flashy performer, internationally known for his flamboyant manner, in a rare (**contemplative, tempestuous**) moment.

5. The psychologist concluded that the subject is (**temperamentally, contemporaneously**) unable to accept defeat without flying into a rage.

6. After the fury of the (**extempore, tempest**) had passed, the air felt strangely calm and clean.

7. A poet observed that while new romance can be agonizingly (**tempestuous, contemplative**), mature love can remain calm.

8. One of the most famous of the many appearances of Halley's Comet was (**temperature, contemporaneous**) with the Battle of Hastings in 1066.

Analogies *In each of the following, circle the item that best completes the comparison.*

1. resplendent is to **shine** as
a. effusive is to gush
b. vestigial is to flow
c. sanguine is to trickle
d. abortive is to cascade

2. patrician is to **hauteur** as
a. lackey is to independence
b. curmudgeon is to amiability
c. sycophant is to servility
d. mountebank is to prescience

3. paean is to **joy** as
a. jeremiad is to sorrow
b. aria is to despair
c. lucubration is to elation
d. polemic is to boredom

4. bromide is to **banal** as
a. non sequitur is to logical
b. philippic is to acerbic
c. elixir is to ineffable
d. vignette is to ribald

5. homily is to **didactic** as
a. corollary is to moot
b. caveat is to cautionary
c. mnemonic is to dogmatic
d. liturgy is to ancillary

6. accolade is to **hero** as
a. melee is to vassal
b. apotheosis is to villain
c. imprecation is to saint
d. obloquy is to poltroon

7. apropos is to **apposite** as
a. ascetic is to hedonistic
b. gargantuan is to dwarfish
c. mercurial is to phlegmatic
d. lugubrious is to lachrymose

8. accoutrements are to **wear** as
a. accessories are to pay
b. utensils are to collect
c. durables are to read
d. comestibles are to eat

9. noxious is to **harm** as
a. portentous is to wealth
b. salubrious is to health
c. bilious is to pleasure
d. traumatic is to ease

10. repartee is to **persiflage** as
a. apogee is to nadir
b. macrocosm is to microcosm
c. probity is to rectitude
d. plethora is to dearth

Choosing the Right Meaning *Read each sentence carefully. Then circle the item that best completes the statement below the sentence.*

So that the medicine goes down "in the most delightful way," children's painkillers
usually consist of an analgesic suspended in an elixir.   (2)

1. The best definition for the word **elixir** in line 2 is
   a. panacea   b. tonic   c. sweet liquid   d. potion

"In bosky shade of highland glen
where dappled sunbeams fling and flicker   (2)
A bonny brook by sylvan sprites is ken
To tumble, traipse, and bravely bicker."
       (A. E. Glug, "Forth to the Firth," IV, 103–106)   (4)

2. In line 4 the word **bicker** most nearly means
   a. plash   b. wrangle   c. quarrel   d. quiver

Until recent times it was the custom for gentlemen to dress in formal wear—including claque and gloves—when attending the opera. (2)

3. The word **claque** in line 2 most nearly means

a. hangers-on   b. fan club   c. flatterers   d. hat

A consequence of the Creek War of 1813–1814 was the deracination of the defeated Creek Indians and their forcible relocation to what is now Oklahoma. (2)

4. In line 1 the word **deracination** is used to mean

a. elimination   b. uprooting   c. eradication   d. surrender

Two-Word Completions

Circle the pair of words that best complete the meaning of each of the following sentences.

1. The verve and _____ with which the leading lady played her part did a great deal to make up for the _____ and indifferent performances turned in by the rest of the cast.

a. casuistry . . . prolix
b. empathy . . . fervid
c. bathos . . . inchoate
d. élan . . . lackluster

2. I began to understand how profoundly John F. Kennedy's assassination had _____ his wife, Jacqueline, when I noticed that she seemed to perform her part in her husband's _____ as if she were sleepwalking.

a. modulated . . . divination
b. traumatized . . . obsequies
c. browbeaten . . . emolument
d. immured . . . homily

3. Since the man has repeatedly shown himself to be a self-seeking _____ who achieves his aims by whatever means are at hand, we have every right to question the _____ of his current dealings.

a. opportunist . . . probity
b. chauvinist . . . hauteur
c. curmudgeon . . . acerbity
d. ascetic . . . protocol

4. Though George Frederick Handel envisaged *Solomon* more as a pageant than as a(n) _____, the underlying didactic purpose of the work is revealed in the deep sense of spirituality with which the composer _____ the music.

a. homily . . . imbued
b. bromide . . . palliated
c. polemic . . . truncated
d. aberration . . . inhibited

5. The _____ of an unsightly larva into a(n) _____ colored monarch butterfly is surely one of the most awesome wonders of nature.

a. vagary . . . effusively
b. acumen . . . fulsomely
c. metamorphosis . . . flamboyantly
d. euphoria . . . zanily

Enriching Your Vocabulary

Read the passage below. Then complete the exercise at the bottom of the page.

The Heritage of Literature

Fine literature ennobles the mind and spirit by enthralling readers with fascinating characters, compelling stories, and absorbing questions to ponder. Literature also contributes to the evolution of language itself. Modern English has borrowed numerous words and phrases from the works of famous and not-so-famous writers. One such word is *quixotic*

Statue of Don Quixote and Sancho Panza, Plaza de España, Madrid, Spain

(Unit 11), which means "extravagantly idealistic." This word derives from the name of the irrepressible main character in *Don Quixote*, the famous comic novel by Spanish Renaissance writer Miguel de Cervantes.

Literature contributes to the development of language by providing a fertile universe of original phrases written by creative authors. From this resource, other writers and speakers borrow expressions and, by using them, distill the concept or idea into familiar words or phrases. What does it mean to be accused of "sour grapes"? This means that a remark came across as belittling or envious. The phrase comes from Aesop's fable "The Fox and the Grapes." It refers to the fox's decision to stop trying to reach for tasty-looking grapes by concluding that they were probably sour anyway, so not worth it.

In Column A below are 6 more words or phrases borrowed from literature. With or without a dictionary, match each word or phrase with its meaning in Column B.

Column A

_____ **1.** bite the hand that feeds you

_____ **2.** ragamuffin

_____ **3.** salad days

_____ **4.** Scrooge

_____ **5.** yahoo

_____ **6.** yeoman service

Column B

a. a miserly and unpleasant person (Source: Charles Dickens's *A Christmas Carol*)

b. a dirty or unkempt child (Source: *A Vision of Piers Plowman*, attributed to William Langland)

c. a crude, brutish, or unrefined person (Source: Jonathan Swift's *Gulliver's Travels*)

d. to show complete ingratitude (Source: Edmund Burke, referring to the public's attitude toward government)

e. one's inexperienced youth (Source: William Shakespeare's *Antony and Cleopatra*, I, v)

f. effective help or assistance, characterized by hard and steady work (Source: William Shakespeare's *Hamlet*, V, ii)

Selecting Word Meanings

*In each of the following groups, circle the word or expression that is **most nearly the same** in meaning as the word in **boldface** type in the given phrase.*

1. took pleasure in pointing out the **solecisms** in my essay
   a. violations of rules
   b. puns and jokes
   c. changing standards
   d. new ideas

2. players who **complemented** each other's abilities
   a. nullified
   b. reinforced and completed
   c. praised
   d. mocked

3. hit upon an answer after long **lucubration**
   a. delay
   b. silence
   c. experimentation
   d. thought

4. an **inchoate** instrument of government
   a. lacking high ideals
   b. in an early stage of development
   c. corrupt
   d. bureaucratic

5. wounded in the **melee**
   a. trap
   b. fight
   c. arm
   d. crisis

6. the **jeremiads** of the old preacher
   a. brilliant oratory
   b. prolonged lamentations
   c. sincere appeals
   d. anecdotes

7. discovered that mathematics was her **forte**
   a. weakness
   b. consuming interest
   c. strong point
   d. nemesis

8. the **noisome** stereotypes of racial bigotry
   a. foul and offensive
   b. expressed in a loud voice
   c. perpetuated
   d. misleading

9. a **morass** of doubts and misunderstandings
   a. swamp
   b. comedy
   c. scholarly analysis
   d. collection

10. **adumbrated** the problems facing us
    a. overcame
    b. avoided
    c. outlined
    d. pondered

11. a **lugubrious** expression on his face
    a. mournful
    b. optimistic
    c. determined
    d. panic-stricken

12. remaining **immaculate** in all circumstances
    a. calm
    b. indifferent
    c. spotless
    d. sagacious

13. whose forces were diminished by **attrition**
    a. unnecessary expenditures
    b. gradual wearing away
    c. natural disasters
    d. flagrant inefficiency

14. the **depredations** of the invaders
a. victories
b. defeats
c. strategic plans
d. plunder and destruction

15. some leeway for interpretation within the **parameters** of the style
a. incidental difficulties
b. determining elements
c. unknown quantities
d. revolutionary ideas

16. critical of their **supine** attitude
a. marked by self-interest
b. superior
c. passive and submissive
d. aggressively uncooperative

17. showed great **prescience** in formulating policies
a. courage
b. determination
c. human sympathy
d. foresight

18. could not fail to recognize her **mellifluous** voice
a. rasping
b. smooth and sweet
c. shrill
d. obviously affected

19. not particularly amused by his attempts at **persiflage**
a. good-natured banter
b. impersonation
c. mime
d. bitter satire

20. willing to overlook our **peccadilloes**
a. minor faults
b. lack of faith
c. blatant dishonesty
d. poor taste

21. annoyed by their **niggardly** methods
a. finicky
b. stingy
c. dishonest
d. insulting

22. singularly **maladroit** in making the arrangements
a. lacking finesse and skill
b. accomplished
c. considerate of others
d. wasteful

23. a **schism** in the ranks of the political party
a. infusion of new strength
b. spread of corruption
c. split
d. mass confusion

24. in the **lexicon** of youth
a. set of values
b. vocabulary
c. time frame
d. inexperience

25. is constantly being misled by **mirages**
a. illusions
b. criminal acts
c. faulty instructions
d. inadequate preparation

26. a group torn apart by **factionalism**
a. quarrels over money
b. lack of communication
c. wild emotionalism
d. partisan differences

27. a **harbinger** of happier days
a. guarantee
b. herald
c. memory
d. enjoyment

28. a **disingenuous** reply
a. lacking in frankness
b. exceptionally creative
c. devoid of human feelings
d. genial and warmhearted

29. furniture selected purely for **utilitarian** purposes
    a. aesthetic
    b. practical
    c. sentimental
    d. economical

30. will not accept such **unconscionable** delays
    a. severely damaging
    b. repeated many times
    c. utterly unjustified
    d. motivated by malice

Words That Describe People

*The words in Column A are used to describe people. In the space before each word, write the **letter** of the item in Column B that identifies it.*

Column A	Column B
_____ **31.** fastidious	**a.** stuck on oneself
_____ **32.** insouciant	**b.** a surly and cantankerous person
_____ **33.** philistine	**c.** carefree; not disposed to worry about dangers or consequences
_____ **34.** narcissistic	
_____ **35.** waggish	**d.** much concerned with details and niceties
_____ **36.** curmudgeon	**e.** practicing strict self-denial
_____ **37.** mountebank	**f.** given to making jokes
_____ **38.** poltroon	**g.** scornful of artistic values or the "finer things in life"
_____ **39.** mercurial	**h.** trickster or phony
_____ **40.** ascetic	**i.** showing contemptible cowardice
	j. showing rapid changes in temperament and attitude

Words Connected with Occupations

*The words in Column A are associated with professions and other occupations. In the space before each word, write the **letter** of the item in Column B that identifies it.*

Column A	Column B
_____ **41.** lachrymose	**a.** diplomats
_____ **42.** therapeutic	**b.** satirical writers
_____ **43.** divination	**c.** writers of sentimental tragedies
_____ **44.** bowdlerize	**d.** doctors and nurses
_____ **45.** lampoon	**e.** actors and actresses
_____ **46.** persona	**f.** concert violinists
_____ **47.** adjudicate	**g.** members of the clergy
_____ **48.** virtuoso	**h.** mediators between quarreling groups
_____ **49.** homily	**i.** fortune-tellers
_____ **50.** protocol	**j.** editors who seek to make classics "more suitable" for young readers

Word Pairs

In the space before each pair of words, write:

S—if the words are synonyms or near-synonyms;
O—if the words are antonyms or near-antonyms;
N—if the words are unrelated in meaning.

_____ **51.** cozen—inveigle

_____ **52.** symptomatic—malleable

_____ **53.** quixotic—practicable

_____ **54.** liaison—protégé

_____ **55.** minuscule—gargantuan

_____ **56.** obloquy—acclaim

_____ **57.** lackluster—drab

_____ **58.** microcosm—macrocosm

_____ **59.** disparate—identical

_____ **60.** bibulous—bilious

_____ **61.** coalesce—amalgamate

_____ **62.** pundit—malcontent

_____ **63.** plebeian—patrician

_____ **64.** hidebound—stodgy

_____ **65.** wanton—licentious

Foreign Words and Phrases

Some words and phrases commonly used in present-day English that are taken directly from foreign languages are listed below. Write the appropriate word or phrase on the line next to each of the following sentences.

fait accompli	sic	mot juste	carte blanche
non sequitur	volte-face	cul-de-sac	ad hoc
sub rosa	hoi polloi	de facto	quid pro quo

66. When they returned home and found the business completely reorganized and functioning successfully, they simply had to accept the new situation. _____

67. The committee has been set up to conduct the investigation, and it will pass out of existence as soon as its job is completed. _____

68. The author added a word to indicate that the misuse of "disinterested" for "uninterested" actually appeared in the book he was quoting. _____

69. It is foolish of you to conclude that she is an expert in "Asian philosophy" just because she made a two-week tour of the Far East. _____

70. The truth is that racial segregation still exists in some parts of the United States, even though it is not sanctioned by law. _____

71. The treaty negotiations will be successful only if each of the parties makes concessions to the other, so that both can feel they are obtaining fair compensation. _____

72. When Mrs. Roth put Larry in charge of the class play, she gave him full authority to select the cast, prepare the sets, and make all other major decisions. _____

73. By my lies and deceptions, I had maneuvered myself into an impossible position from which I could neither advance nor retreat. _____

74. When Fran referred to him as an "intellectual snob," I felt that she had found the perfect epithet on which to skewer his pretentious personality. _____

75. I was shocked when he abandoned the cause he had backed so long and became an advocate of a diametrically opposed program. _____

Word Associations

*In each of the following, circle the word or expression that best completes the meaning of the sentence or answers the question, with particular reference to the meaning of the word in **boldface** type.*

76. Your situation might well be described as **precarious** if you were
a. lolling in a hammock
b. hanging from the edge of a cliff
c. playing tennis with a weak opponent
d. attending the Senior Prom

77. To say that a person is **bickering** over the terms of a contract implies
a. praise for being careful
b. disapproval of the contract provisions
c. complete indifference
d. criticism for being petty

78. From a renowned **raconteur** you would expect
a. a superb dinner
b. an entertaining story
c. expert legal advice
d. the perfect crime

79. An **empirical** analysis of a problem is based primarily on
a. the laws of chance
b. preconceived ideas
c. wishful thinking
d. experience

80. If you refer to someone's reactions as **maudlin**, you are
a. expressing sympathy
b. complaining of excessive sentimentality
c. showing utter indifference
d. charging deliberate misrepresentation

81. Deeds of **derring-do** are associated particularly with
a. knights-errant
b. politicians
c. suburban commuters
d. scholars and intellectuals

82. What advice might you give to a person who is guilty of a **tautology**?
a. "See your doctor immediately."
b. "Don't repeat yourself."
c. "Stop that abusive language."
d. "Speak more slowly and distinctly."

83. A person who has just received a **lagniappe** would most likely
a. take some medication
b. say, "Thanks!"
c. seek revenge
d. mend his or her ways

84. Which of the following indicates **kudos**?
a. "Get out of my life!"
b. "Do what I say, not what I do."
c. "What have I done to deserve this?"
d. "You're the greatest!"

85. People who indulge in **casuistry** are most likely
a. overeating
b. spreading rumors
c. splitting hairs
d. feeling sorry for themselves

86. People who are affected by **xenophobia** are
a. fond of rich food
b. afraid of heights
c. suspicious of foreigners
d. unlucky in love

87. Which of the following might properly be described as a **faux pas**?
a. scoring the winning touchdown
b. attending a formal party in blue jeans
c. eating a hearty breakfast
d. learning to water-ski

88. We would expect **aficionados** of the opera to
a. picket the local opera house
b. attend opera performances often
c. sing the lead role in *Carmen*
d. never go to an opera

89. The expression "**vicissitudes** of life" refers to life's
a. beginning and end   b. ups and downs   c. pleasures   d. side issues

90. What is the prevailing mood of a speaker who delivers a **philippic**?
a. smug self-satisfaction
b. joyful approbation
c. bitter disapproval
d. impartiality

91. Which of the following best describes the mood and atmosphere of a **gothic** novel?
a. bright and cheerful
b. dark and gloomy
c. zany and slapstick
d. sophisticated and satirical

92. A person who may properly be described as an **opportunist** is trying hard to
a. help others
b. get ahead at any cost
c. maintain law and order
d. stay young and beautiful

93. Which of the following expresses the attitude of a **dogmatic** person?"
a. "I may be wrong."
b. "I'm waiting for more evidence."
c. "What do you think about it?"
d. "I'm right, and that's that!"

94. Which of the following would be most likely to accept a philosophy of **nihilism**?
a. a deeply religious person
b. an accomplished physicist
c. a conservative
d. a sweeping critic of the social order

95. A **flamboyant** personality suggests a
a. demure little wren   b. bold eagle   c. perky robin   d. showy peacock

96. An editorial writer who refers to a strike as **internecine** believes that
a. the strike will be successful
b. all parties involved will suffer greatly
c. labor is justified in calling the strike
d. the strike will end soon

97. Which of the following might you seek to **deracinate**?
a. fun and games
b. old friends and good companions
c. tree stumps and bad habits
d. patience and fortitude

98. Which of the following is typical of **nepotism**?
a. giving good jobs to relatives
b. donating large sums to charity
c. advancing the public interest
d. suffering delusions of persecution

99. What would be the most logical thing to do if you were in a **labyrinth**?
a. sit down and enjoy the show
b. deliver a eulogy to the departed
c. start the motor and drive off
d. try to find your way out

100. You would be likely to regard it as a **contretemps** if you
a. improved your vocabulary
b. won first prize in an essay contest
c. helped your classmates
d. did poorly on this final test

The following tabulation lists all the basic words taught in the various units of this book, as well as those introduced in the *Vocabulary of Vocabulary, Working with Analogies, Building with Classical Roots,* and *Enriching Your Vocabulary* sections. Words taught in the units are printed in **boldface** type. The number following each entry indicates the page on which the word is first introduced. Exercises and review materials in which the word also appears are not cited.